KING COPPER

KING COPPER

South Wales and the Copper Trade
1584–1895

RONALD REES

UNIVERSITY OF WALES PRESS
CARDIFF
2000

British Library Cataloguing-in-Publication Data.
A catalogue record for this book is available from the British Library.

ISBN 0–7083–1588–7 (hardback)
0–7083–1589–5 (paperback)

The author and publishers wish to acknowledge with thanks the financial support of the following for publication of this book:
Mr David Grenville Thomas, chairman of Navigator Exploration Corp. of Canada, formerly of Neath and Morriston.
West Glamorgan Archive Service.

Typeset by Action Publishing Technology, Gloucester
Printed in Great Britain by
Cambrian Printers, Aberystwyth

Contents

ᐢ

Illustrations

అ

To
Matthew and Karen Rees
and to my friend
Howard Chapman of Skewen

Foreword

The idea for a book on the impact of copper smelting upon society and environment in south Wales came from two disparate sources several years ago. The first was a romantic novel, *Copper Kingdom*, by Iris Gower who then lived in Manselton, an industrial suburb of Swansea that once was in the heart of the smelting district. One of the more dramatic incidents in the novel is a 'copper smoke' trial in Carmarthen attended by copper workers who had walked the twenty-five miles from Swansea. Sensing a story, I went to the newspapers of the day and in March 1833 issues of Swansea's *Cambrian* and Carmarthen's *Welshman* I found the detailed accounts of the trial I was looking for. Neither reporter referred to a march of Swansea copper workers to Carmarthen but if the workers were not there in person they were certainly there in spirit, for had the action (brought by aggrieved Tawe Valley farmers) been successful it might have threatened their livelihoods. Here, clearly, was the beginning of a story and a little digging revealed that there was more. The Carmarthen trial was the but the first action in a long campaign conducted by farmers, landowners and concerned citizens against the coppermasters.

The obvious frame for the story was the nineteenth-century debate over public health in and around Britain's towns and cities; protection of amenity and environment were of some concern but they were not yet major issues. Happily for me, the public health debate in Swansea found a gifted modern interpreter working in that most restricting of forms, a postgraduate thesis. Gerald Fielder's study of public health and hospital administration in nineteenth-century Swansea is a rare phenomenon, a work of detailed, rigorous scholarship written with verve and style. Had Fielder chosen to concentrate on the copper industry there would have been no need for this book.

My other great debt is to the sponsors of the book. Few histories can be written and published without public or private subsidy. For their generous grants, I am most grateful to the West Glamorgan Archive Service and to David Grenville Thomas, formerly of Neath and Morriston, and now of Navigator Explorations, Vancouver, British Columbia.

RONALD REES

Introduction

❧

Overlooking the dock in Swansea's attractive Maritime Quarter is a weathered bronze statue of the city's most celebrated entrepreneur: John Henry Vivian, Fellow of the Royal Society, Member of Parliament and, in his day, coppermaster of world renown. If bronze eyes could be made to see, they would be startled by the view presented to them. Although Vivian died in 1855, four years before the official opening of the dock, he would have been familiar with the sights and sounds that characterized it: wharves, warehouses and storage sheds echoing with the reassuring clatter of commerce, long lines of labourers wheeling barrowloads of copper ore and a waterfront bristling with the masts of sturdy barques acquainted with the sea lanes of the Atlantic and the Pacific. Today the dock is still, at least for the winter months. The dock-side is home to a maritime/industrial museum and an apartment complex, and the dock itself to a gay flotilla of pleasure craft.

The view beyond the dock and up the river that flows into the bay beside it would be just as disconcerting. A valley floor that in Vivian's day was 'cram-jammed', as one reporter put it then, with furnaces, chimneys and mountainous heaps of slag and furnace ash, has been swept clean of heavy industry. Even the Vivian name, which used to hang on every lip, is fading from memory. The family has gone from the city and its name now is attached only to a pair of statues, an art gallery, a handful of streets and a pub.

So thoroughly has the old industrial landscape been effaced that visitors to the city must take it on faith that in the first half of the nineteenth century Swansea was copper smelter not just to Britain, but to the world. A galaxy of copper works stretching from Pembrey and Llanelli in the west to Port Talbot and Taibach in the east, but heavily massed in the valley of the Tawe, produced virtually all of Britain's copper and, until about 1860, more than half of the world's. By any measure it was a remarkable industrial concentration; it produced wealth for the coppermasters and, by the standards of the day, good wages and decent housing and schools for their workers. In Swansea and the neighbouring towns, copper unquestionably ruled.

Yet that reign, though imperious, was not untroubled. Copper ores are notoriously impure and smelting them produced not only large quantities of solid waste, or slag, but clouds of toxic gases that killed trees and crops, and poisoned both pastures and the animals that fed on them. In all cases the smelters, bound to supplies of Welsh coal, were built on farmed and settled land. The town/country dichotomy has seldom been so clearly exposed, and farmers and landowners, who were understandably distressed, resorted periodically to 'the gentlemen of the long robe'. In south Wales the legal proceedings were never a threat to the sovereignty of the copper industry but responsible owners went to great lengths to eliminate the poisons from the smoke. When these efforts failed they built tall stacks in an attempt to send the smoke clear of adjacent farmlands. Other owners, however, did nothing, taking cover behind permissive anti-smoke legislation and the Victorian adage that without muck there can be no money.

The chief cause of unrest was damage to property but there was also some apprehension about the effects of copper smoke on human health. Visitors to the copperworks towns wondered how smoke that was virulent enough to scour glass and kill plants within a matter of hours could fail to damage human tissue. But both owners and workers, protective of profits in the one case, and livelihoods in the other, insisted on the harmlessness of the smoke. Behind them stood the tradesmen, merchants and professional men who, whenever copper smoke was attacked, closed ranks around the copper interests. Most vigilant of all were Swansea's physicians who either denied that copper smoke was in any way harmful to health or, in the absence of certain knowledge of the causes and transmission of disease, ascribed to it antiseptic and prophylactic powers. A few held that the smoke districts were *cordons sanitaires* that cholera and typhus – those twin scourges of the Victorian poor – were unable to breach.

Health commissioners and statisticians of disease and death eventually dispelled the myth of copper smoke as a prophylactic, but the smoke remained a will o' the wisp that eluded the grasp of the law. Until the middle of the nineteenth century, science and technology were helpless before the most harmful of the gases, and in Swansea itself neither statistics nor reasoned argument had any effect on municipal attitudes and policies. The local board of health systematically ignored even the limited anti-smoke legislation that was available to it. Chemistry and technology eventually found a way of reducing the levels of toxic gases in the smoke, but by the time they had done so the condition of the copper industry was considered too fragile for the remedy to be applied. Even weakened and ailing monarchs have power. In Swansea and the neighbouring towns, copper remained king to the end.

1

Creating the Kingdom

A Secret Art and Mystery

Until deprived of its magic by modern metallurgy, smelting copper was an arcane or mysterious art. Men who could take rough, dull ore and distil from it soft, shining metal that could be beaten into leaves, rolled into fine sheets or drawn into wire, were near-sorcerers who had once been above the law: the smith's hammer was a universal symbol of power and in ancient Greece as in Gretna Green an oath taken over an anvil could not be broken. By the Renaissance, metal-making had lost most of its mystical associations but it was far from being a commonplace art.[1] Copper is an intractable ore and in Europe only the Germans had mastered the techniques of locating and mining the mineral-bearing veins.[2] It was Germans, too, in a world where banking, money and industrial organization were becoming more complex, who understood the principles of capital investment and were skilled in the delicate matter of allocating shares and profits among the interested parties in mining and metal-making ventures.[3]

The British had learned how to mine coal and tin, and make wrought iron but at working and refining the more difficult ores – copper, gold, silver and zinc – they were novices. 'High Germans are more inventive', wrote an admiring Maurice Wynn early in the seventeenth century, 'and no nation can come near them in the mechanical arts.'[4] With energy and enterprise to spare, and technical skills to market, German engineers, miners and metallurgists were constantly on the alert for promising ventures at home or abroad and it was only a matter of time until the curves of English needs and German expertise intersected. The catalyst was armaments. Guns were made of iron, copper or bell metal – a mixture of copper and tin – and the copper for English ordnance, as well as the ordnance-makers, had to be imported. Henry VIII's gun-makers, who were mostly from Flanders and France, frequently ran out of copper, forcing Henry to defend English shores with cannon bought from continental manufacturers. The situation could not endure.[5]

Although defence was the spur, another, gentler need lay behind the establishment of a home-based copper industry. Wool had been a staple of England's economy since the twelfth century, and before wool could be spun the fibres had to be separated or 'carded'. The cards were flat pieces of wood with handles on one side and brass wire teeth set in leather on the other. The raw wool was placed between the cards and worked and combed until the fibres were disentangled. Until the end of the sixteenth century most of the cards were imported, and even if they were home-made the brass wire was usually manufactured abroad. To make wool cards in Britain meant finding copper and calamine to make the brass, and importing German machines to manufacture the wire.[6]

As well as threatening the stability of a staple industry, dependence on foreign suppliers also drained Britain's wealth. In economic matters, mercantilist ideas of self-sufficiency prevailed. A nation that produced most of its own raw materials and manufactures enjoyed a favourable balance of payments, the best of all possible economic worlds. To husband the nation's wealth the Tudors encouraged mining and metal-making, but to make headway they needed German miners and metallurgists. So developed a complementary arrangement that satisfied both parties: the English looked to Germany for capital and skill, and the Germans to England for privileges and royal grants.[7]

The first serious overtures were made by Elizabeth I and Lord Cecil, her Secretary of State. 'Foreign Chymists and Mineral Masters' were invited to exploit British minerals provided they returned the favour by instructing British subjects in 'the Mineral Arts and Sciences'. Copper was to be mined under the aegis of the Mines Royal Society, so named because until the end of seventeenth century the Crown insisted upon its exclusive right to mine the ores of metals needed for coinage: gold, silver, quicksilver, copper and tin.

Incorporated by royal charter in 1568, the Society at first concentrated its efforts in Cumberland where lead, silver and iron had been worked since the eleventh century, and copper since the thirteenth. In a letter to Francis Bacon, in 1614, the Lord Chief Justice wrote that 'upon discovery of certain copper mines (at Keswick) in the time of Queen Elizabeth, great care and labour were taken to draw men of skill and experience out of parts beyond the seas to work the same'. In all, some 300–400 workmen left Augsburg for Keswick and in bringing their works 'to good perfection', noted the Lord Chief Justice, they produced enough copper for England's armaments and freed the realm from the 'favour of foreign princes'.

Although Cumberland remained the centre of Mines Royal operations, the Society's interests were kingdom-wide. By the 1580s it had begun mining in Cornwall, long a source of tin, but known also to be rich in copper ore. In charge of operations in Cornwall were Ulrich Frosse and

Hans Haring, both of whom had been sent down from Keswick. Mining in Cornwall was extremely difficult: spring-waters poured into the newly dug shafts, and tight-fisted backers (who had leased the Cornish mineral rights from the Mines Royal Company) were so sparing with funds that from time to time the men had to work without pay. Copper lodes, unlike tin, are seldom near the surface and Frosse's cries that to mine profitably was to mine deeply, and that the expense must be borne, frequently fell on deaf ears. Frosse eventually found ore of good quality but by the time he had done so his frustrating Cornish sojourn was almost over.[8]

The Move into Wales

In July 1584 Frosse was told to arrange for the transport of Cornish ores to the Society's new melting house, of which he was to be manager, at 'Neth in Wales'.[9] In Cornwall timber for charcoal might well have been scarce whereas Neath (Castell-nedd), which was only a short sea voyage from Cornwall, was surrounded by woodland. To the west was the forest of Coedffranc, and in the valley just above the town were outcrops of easily mined coal.[10] When mixed with charcoal these proved to be an effective furnace fuel. But even allowing for Neath's patent advantages as a site for smelting Cornish copper, geography alone might not have been the the only determinant of location. William Herbert, the first earl of Pembroke and lord of the manors of Neath, was also a principal shareholder of the Mines Royal Society.

On his arrival at Neath in the autumn of 1585, Ulrich Frosse would have found a town still medieval in form. Initially a Norman fortress built on a terrace 4 miles above the mouth of the Nedd, the settlement in the centuries since the Conquest had acquired a church, a guildhall, a market, a handful of streets and a population of a few hundred people.[11] By sixteenth-century standards Neath was a place worth noting, but an Elizabethan recorder in 1562 had eyes only for its economy: 'a pill within a baye for small boats where there is a myne and Trade of coals'.

Downstream from Neath, near the ferry at the mouth of the river, was a small cluster of houses, and half a mile to the west the remains of a great Cistercian abbey surrendered to the Crown in 1539. On dissolution, the abbey's jewels, plate, cash and other treasures had been transferred to the royal treasury, the roof removed, the lead melted down into pigs for the King's needs, the walls plundered for building stone and the productive abbey farms placed in lay hands. In 1585 the once magnificent abbey church was a roofless shell whose outbuildings, in little more than a century, would house a metal factory.

Early historians of the copper trade placed the first Welsh copper works near the abbey but current historians now favour a site two miles above the town where the Nedd is joined by the Dulais. Just above the point of confluence, in a secluded cleft of the Dulais valley, is a waterfall powerful enough to have worked the giant bellows that were needed to provide blast for the copper furnaces. The Nedd is tidal as far as the 'bend' at the mouth of the Dulais (Aberdulais), and the Cornish ores, shipped in vessels of shallow draught, were probably carried there on the flood. If not – and there is speculation that a monastic weir a mile or so downstream might have impeded the passage of Cornish boats – the ores could have been unloaded at the town quay, just below the river bridge, and taken to Aberdulais by pack animal. In Elizabeth I's state papers for 1585 there is a record of 'John Bwaple, one of Wales, [who came] w'h his bark for a frayght of Copp'owre for Wales, and did delyver hem . . . 15 Tunn & 8 hundred of copp'owre'. The vessel most likely to have been used for the shipment of ores was the herring buss, a small 50-ton fishing vessel of shallow draft that was also used for carrying cargo.[12]

'Divers Hurtfull Humours'

In the wooded cleft of the Dulais valley, safe presumably from the prying eyes of the townspeople, a handful of skilled German workers, which included a 'copper maker', a 'refiner', an 'undermelter' and a 'Douch [Dutch] carpenter', all transferred to Aberdulais from the Society's smelting works at Keswick, set about the painstaking and carefully guarded process of extracting metal from copper ore. Aberdulais, as Customer Thomas Smythe had assured Ulrich Frosse, was even 'more for yo'r quietness than Cornwall is'. Thomas Smythe, to whom Frosse was both a 'friend and loving servant', was a lessee of Mines Royal mineral rights in Wales.

Before leaving Cornwall the 'green' ore would have been, in the vernacular of the copper trade, stamped, picked and dressed: that is, reduced to nodules, sifted and washed free of earth, sand and other loose materials. To drive out the sulphur and arsenic which George Nedham, a Mines Royal shareholder and apprentice smelter at Keswick, remarked were 'naturally bred in copper ores', the ore had to be heated or calcined in furnaces hot enough to roast but not melt it.[13] Calcining released the volatile sulphur, which 'goeth away very violently', and arsenic, 'w'ch is a vere daungerous ayer or savor'. After each calcining the ore was drenched with water, a treatment that released even more arsenic and sulphur in plumes of steam and white smoke that on still, clear days, spiralled upward with disarming picturesqueness. 'Water doth not onely draw out the vitriall and coppris from the ore', wrote Nedham, 'but also divers other hurtfull humours, being by nature enemyes of the copper.'[14] The 'hurtfull humours', as the people of Neath would discover, were enemies of more than copper.

Because of the low quality – by premodern standards – of Cornish ores, as many as sixteen roastings over many weeks had at first been necessary. But in 1581 Joachim Gaunse, manager of the smelting works at Keswick, reduced the roasting stage to four days. Frosse recorded that since his coming from Keswick, where he had visited his English wife and their four children, he had acquired 'such further knowledg of the nature of all o'r copp'ures' that he would be able to 'kill all the corupt humors that be in them, and therby bring out more copper than heretofore hath byn, and w'th lesser charge'.

Once free of sulphur and arsenic, the ore was then melted in closed furnaces and the copper, in stages, separated from the iron, silica and other base metals. To draw the maximum amount of metal from the ore and reduce to a minimum the amount lost through slag and fire required great skill and experience. At each melting the slags and fluxes were skimmed off the surface leaving the heavier and progressively purer metal at the bottom of the furnace. To smelt (draw the metal from) a low-grade ore could take as many as seven or eight meltings lasting up to three days and nights.

Shortly after his arrival at Neath, Frosse reported that copper smelting 'doth goe reasonablye well forward' and that he and his men had found a way of melting 24 hundredweight of ore daily in a single furnace, and spending not above eight sacks of charcoal and three horseloads of coal. As manager of a smelting house Frosse seems to have been peerless. At Neath he greatly reduced the smelting period, attributing the economy to 'a metchen [method] which we have found out by chance'. By mixing hard ores with soft, and rich with poor, he discovered that the varied impurities in the ores served as fluxes that allowed even the difficult ores to be reduced in a shorter time and with smaller losses of metal. To confirm his discovery, he wrote 'Fro Nethe' to the overseer of the Cornish mines, 'desiringe yow from hence forwarde to send such owres as yow have w'th as much speed as maye be, not caring what owre it is'. And in March 1587 he reported that 'melting many sorts of ewres together is the most proffet, and will melt a greatayll souner'. Using both charcoal and coal, Frosse found he could melt more than a ton of ore in seven hours, and with virtually no waste. In a letter to William Carnsewe, a Cornish squire, he explained how he had taken more than a ton of cinders, the residue of smelting processes, and melted them down.

They produced less than an ounce of copper, a sure 'saigne' that he had brought all the metal out of the ore.

Because Neath men knew nothing of the techniques of smelting, only minor and unskilled operations would have been entrusted to them if, indeed, any were employed. There is no evidence of any ill-feeling between the people of the town and the German copper workers. At Keswick, where the German presence was so much greater, there were riots. Queen Elizabeth had to urge justices of the peace 'to repress the assaults, murders and outrages on the Almain miners lately come there for the purpose of searching for and working minerals'. In spite of Frosse's accomplishments, the significance of the Aberdulais venture lay in what it portended, not in what it achieved. Shortage of ore was a problem from the outset and Frosse's successive reductions in the length of the smelting period simply exacerbated it by increasing the demand. From time to time the furnaces lay idle, to Frosse's chagrin. In June 1585 he complained that operations had been delayed for fourteen days because of the 'lack of good store of rich ewres'. And in October of the same year, John Otes, manager of the mines in Cornwall, reported: 'for my lyffe I could not gett any owre from St. Yeust to St. Ives to fraight hem for Wales, but went awaye w'hout any.' Furnaces were again idle in 1586–7; Frosse wrote: 'Wee have done nothing all this winter for lake of ewre.' With no steam engines to pump water out of the workings, copper mining in Cornwall tended to be a summer, or at least a dry-season occupation. Capital as well as ore was occasionally in short supply; in November 1585 Frosse had to borrow locally, 'from one Pasco Wynser', to pay the wages of his workmen.

For how long Frosse and his German compatriots were able to continue smelting at Aberdulais is not known. The last recorded metal shipment bears the date 1605 and by c.1660 Mines Royal smelting operations had moved three miles downstream to a site near the abbey where the River Clydach joins the Nedd. At the new site, coal was as readily available as it had been in the Dulais valley, and cargoes of ore could be unloaded at the very gates of the works. By 1694 Mines Royal smelters were supplying a nearby copper battery mill – which hammered the copper pigs into sheets – and by 1708 a Bristol man (Dr Lane) had set up a rival smelter about half a mile upriver.

Sir Humphrey Mackworth

The young copper kingdom was growing, but its true architect at Neath had not yet arrived on the scene. In 1686 Sir Humphrey Mackworth of

Bentley in Worcestershire married Mary Evans, heiress of the Gnoll estate in Neath and the Pencrug estate in Monmouthshire. Though not practising at the time of his marriage, Sir Humphrey was a distinguished barrister. He had been knighted at twenty-seven for services to Charles II, and at twenty-eight he was chosen to present an address of welcome to the new monarch, James II. His reasons for withdrawing from the Bar and settling in Wales were never disclosed, but his many critics and enemies contended that marriage to Mary Evans was the first step on the path to industrial autocracy in Glamorgan. Late in life Mackworth declared that as a young man his ambition had been to 'outdo all the works in the kingdom'. His Whig detractors labelled him the 'Church-Tory Knight of the Gnoll' while for a local lampoonist he was a mere opportunist, '[a man with] the art to make the Lady part with a good old ancient estate'.[15]

At the time of his marriage to Mary Evans the Gnoll estate brought in fewer than £2,000 a year, so to match the income to his ambitions Mackworth had to employ great energy and invention. Graduating from coal mining to copper smelting, Mackworth transformed Neath. He took advantage of a slump in trade to wrest the tenancy of local coal mines from the Neath burgesses and followed this, in 1695, by building a copper works on the Cryddan brook about half a mile south of the town. At first he used Cornish ores, then – to circumvent the problem of irregular supplies that had bedevilled Ulrich Frosse – ores from copper and lead mines in Cardigan in which he had acquired a controlling interest. Mackworth's energy and enterprise, as Francis Klingender pointed out, inspired one of the earliest panegyrics to an industrial entrepreneur. In 1710 Thomas Yalden addressed the following lines to Sir Humphrey:

> Thy famed inventions, Mackworth, most adorn
> The Miners Art, and make the best return.
> Thy speedy sails, and useful Engines show
> A Genius Richer than the mines below.[16]

Using funds raised through a lottery, Mackworth built canals, quays and docks. The furnaces at Melincryddan were less than half a mile from the river so coastal vessels of 80–100 tons could berth nearby. Tramlines led from the quays to the works and from the works to the pits, and along them trundled ingenious sail-driven trams, 'speedy Sails' that, as an admiring William Waller remarked, allowed one horse to do the work of ten and one man the work of twenty. They were the first sailing engines, so Waller claimed, to be built 'not for curiosity and vain applause, but for real Profit'. The trams carried coal to the smelting furnaces and to the holds of emptied ore boats for shipment to Cornwall. But, ominously for Neath's future as a port, Mackworth's own vessel, the *Mines*

Adventurer, was not among them. At 120 tons she was too large to ascend the river and had to be unloaded at a point near the mouth and the ore brought upstream in lighters to the Melincryddan dock. In its flood-plain section the Nedd, whose flow is slowed by exposure to stiff westerly and south-westerly winds, is subject to silting.

From the outset, one of Mackworth's chief difficulties had been the absence locally of skilled labour. Apart from copper workers at the Mines Royal Neath Abbey works, who would have been bound and sworn to secrecy, there were no workers capable of manning the copper works or the mines. Coalworks lost 'for want of air' could not, for 'want of Artists in that Country', be recovered.[17] Skilful colliers, familiar with the techniques of air circulation, timbering, waggoning and cutting had to be brought in from Shropshire and Derbyshire. Trained copper workers were in even shorter supply. In December 1704 a select committee of the Company of Mine Adventurers (of which Mackworth was the president, principal shareholder and manager) declared 'that more smelters and Refiners and other Manufacturers of Oar may be employed in the works of this Company to a great Advantage'. And in June 1706 Mackworth was empowered 'to make such Contracts or Bargains for Smelters, Refiners, or other Artists' as he should deem necessary. Each was indentured under what were termed proper agreements and each man given a week's wages and a bounty of 10 shillings. Some of the men employed at Melincryddan were described as 'Strangers in the Country and many of them above two hundred Miles from Home'. The 'strangers', some of whom were undoubtedly German, trained local workmen who soon became 'able Men bred up and instructed by skilful Persons'.

From each of its workers the company required an oath of fidelity and a bond or covenant binding them for fixed terms of at least a year. As well as being legally bound to the company, a bonded man was also free from danger of impressment; Britain then was at war with France. The practice angered Mackworth's enemies. One of the most implacable of these, Sir Edward Mansell of Margam, noted: 'It has been and still is the Practice of Sir Humphrey Mackworth ... to receive and entertain ... Strangers and Idle Persons, without Certificates or Testimonials of their last legal Settlements' who signed the various bonds and instruments 'only as a colour to keep them in the Parish and from being taken into His Majesty's Service'.[18]

So scarce was manpower, and so dangerous were working conditions in the mines, that the company had to employ as labourers condemned pirates and prisoners who had been pardoned on condition that they apprentice themselves to the company for five years. In 1700 Mackworth applied to the judges on the Norfolk circuit to allow 'Jaylors to convey condemned prisoners to Neath'. In due course, seventeen felons were pardoned and ten of them were sent to Neath. While the burgesses of Neath seem to have been tolerant of skilled workers from Germany and elsewhere, released prisoners were another matter. In 1705 the 'principal inhabitants' of Neath complained bitterly that the men employed in the coal works and smelting works were

for the most part disorderly livers, often spending two or three daies together in drinking and other debaucherys: and some of them after yt they have married wives and gott children have left them a Burthen on the Borough and Parish: and others after they have debauched young women and gott them with child, and others after they have run in debt have removed into other places and left the parish and their creditors in the lurch.[19]

For Mackworth's rivals and enemies, some of whom were justices of the peace, the public animus against him presented a golden opportunity for revenge. In 1705 the justices issued a warrant for the impressment of a number of Mines Adventurers workmen, bound or not, 'that came from other Parishes or Places'. About a dozen smelters, refiners and colliers were caught and impressed while the remainder, in 'a great Terror', fled to the hills leaving 'Metal unwrought and the Furnaces spoiled'. To complete the rout, the Neath justices threatened to remove from the parish all those workmen who had come from elsewhere. The action clearly was an attempt to intimidate the skilled workers whom Mackworth had brought from Shropshire and Derbyshire. Many of these, it was reported cryptically, then decided 'to enter the Service of . . . other Persons in that Neighbourhood'.[20]

In spite of fearsome rivalry, the bankruptcy of the Company of Mines Adventurers, loss of the Cardiganshire mines and impeachment before the Bar of the Whig-dominated House of Commons for alleged peculations and violations of the company's charter, Mackworth managed to retain ownership of the Melincryddan works until his death in 1727. For want of capital, the works lay idle for three years (1709–12) but in 1713 the irrepressible Mackworth floated another company of mineral manufacturers which not only revived the Melincryddan works but built battery mills for making copper and brass utensils on the Gnoll estate. In its 1720 prospectus the company proclaimed Neath's role as the cradle of the Welsh copper industry:

Few know how to refine and make Copper fit for Brass kettles and other Brass Manufactures, but here [at Neath] the Partners have Artists of long Standing and experience, who can make Copper fit for all Uses, and can refine the worst and coarsest Copper . . . at a small Charge, and make it fit for the said Manufactures.[21]

After Mackworth's death the Melincryddan works languished, his descendants being either uninterested in copper or more interested in the coal trade. The works were leased to several different operators and effectively closed in 1796 when Lady Molly Mackworth, who inherited the Gnoll estate upon the death of her husband (Sir Robert Mackworth), refused to grant a lease to the Mines Royal Company. She withheld consent on grounds that smoke from the works would 'waste' Gnoll House.[22] It was the first action against copper smoke taken by a Welsh landowner and it led, in effect, to the decline of copper smelting within the borough of Neath. Though the beneficiary of Sir Humphrey Mackworth, and a century of copper smelting, Lady Molly Mackworth had cause for alarm. When the Reverend Richard Warner visited Gnoll House in 1798, he noted the danger to the house and gardens and the long tree-lined drives planted with limes, holly, box, yew, sycamore, walnut and cherry brought from Bristol. The 'great manufactories' lay no more than a mile to the south-west of them and, given the prevalence of westerly and southerly winds, they must be wrapped 'in highly disagreeable and pernicious fumes, three-fourths of the year'.[23]

A Reluctant Capital

In spite of vindictive rivals, hurtful humours, labour shortages and uncertain supplies of ore, copper smelting was attractive to would-be entrepreneurs. Demand for copper and brass – a copper/zinc alloy – increased steadily during the eighteenth century. Besides ordnance, copper and brass were needed for coinage, industrial vats and containers, rollers for making textiles, and household articles ranging from kettles, candlesticks and pans to buttons, buckles, pins and thimbles. A soft, workable metal that could resist heat and steam pressure was also indispensable to the makers of the new pumps and engines. Cylinders, steam valves and cocks, grease caps, gauge covers, whistles and other accessories were all made of copper or brass. Stephenson's Rocket, built in 1829, had a copper firebox, copper tubes for carrying the steam and a variety of brass fittings. There was also a growing market overseas. By the middle of the eighteenth century, rolled copper and brass sheets were being made for metal workers in India; copper vats, containers and utensils for West Indian rum and sugar makers; and short 'copper rods' and horse-shoe shaped bronze 'manillas' for African slavers. Copper rods and bronze manillas or bangles, which were the currency of the slave trade, were made at Penclawdd and in the White Rock works at Swansea.[24]

Changes on the supply side also stimulated the growth of the industry.

The removal in 1689 of the Mines Royal monopoly on the mining of copper unleashed fresh enterprise and intensified the search for ore. In Cornwall deeper mining exposed copper ores that lay beneath the tin, and the introduction of gunpowder for blasting gave miners the power to extract them. Pumping engines made by Boulton and Watt solved the problem of water in the mines and did much to increase their productivity. There was also, late in the seventeenth century, a critical development in the technique of smelting. By making a furnace that burned coal only, William Coster, a Bristol and Redbrook smelter, freed first lead smelting then copper smelting from their dependence on charcoal.

Neath may have cradled the Welsh copper industry but it could hardly have expected to preserve a monopoly. Suitable furnace coals lay all around and all places in the region were equally convenient to Cornish ores and the metal markets of Birmingham and London. Almost any settlement near a harbour or a river mouth could rival Neath, and in time several would. Before the end of the eighteenth century there were copper works at Taibach, Penclawdd and, most notably, at Swansea. When Daniel Defoe visited Swansea in the 1720s he found a bustling port that, like Neath, conducted a lively trade in coal:

> Swanzy is . . . a very considerable town for trade, with a very good harbur. Here is also a very good trade for coals, and culm, which they export to all parts of Somerset, Devon, and Cornwall, and even to Ireland; so that sometimes may be seen a hundred sail of ships at a time loading coals here.[25]

Not only was Swansea busier and, with roughly 1,500 people, bigger than Neath, it was also more Anglicized and – as befitted the birthplace of Richard 'Beau' Nash – more cosmopolitan. Though a coal port, the town was attractive and its setting, at the mouth of the Tawe and adjacent to a fine sandy beach at the head of a magnificent bay, splendid. Unlike Neath, which was backed by high moorland, forest and marsh, Swansea lay at the threshold of a rich agricultural area: the beckoning lands of Gower (Gŵyr). With assets like these it had no intention of remaining a coal port, especially when, as Defoe noted, it also had those elixirs of eighteenth-century life – mineral waters:

> Theer are lately mineral waters found at Swanzy, which are reported to be of great efficacy in fluxes, and Haemorrhages of all sorts. Consumptions, if not too far gone, diabetes, palsies, rheumatisms, dropsies, and other distempers, are said to fall before these styptick and restorative waters.

By way of reprimand to all purveyors of healing airs, waters and medicines, Defoe added that while 'they may certainly have very good effects in many difficult cases; . . . it is doing an injury to the reputation of any medicine in the World, to make it a "Catholicon", and good for everything'.

Whatever the limitations of Swansea's airs and waters, there was no denying the town's fitness as a location for smelting copper. As at Neath, the coal measures came down to the sea and the coals were chiefly of the free-burning semi-bituminous kind that made little ash to clog the grates of the furnaces. But also available were softer bituminous coals that clung to the freer-burning coals in the reverberatory furnaces. When used alone, the freer-burning coals tended to slip through the furnace bars, but if mixed with about a quarter of their weight of soft bituminous coal they formed a layer of clinker about a foot thick that rested comfortably on them.

Welsh coals were irresistible to Cornish ores and – smelting then being profligate of coal – the ores came readily to them. Swansea coals were also easy to mine and, being near the river, they were cheap to transport. Haulage costs for heavy materials over eighteenth-century roads were prohibitive. Most roads were merely rough, pot-holed tracks and coal hauled over them doubled in price every few miles. Copper works as a result were never far from places where coal was mined, or from rivers and canals on which it could be carried cheaply. Coals at a distance from 'navigation' had no value and they were worked, usually from holes scraped in the sides of hills, only if needed as household fuel. The twin advantages of coal and navigation impressed themselves on H. P. Wyndham on his tour of Wales in 1774. The 'plenty' of coals in and around Swansea and 'the convenience of exportation', he noted, have 'induced the copper companies to prefer this spot to all others'.[26]

Along the Tawe, coal seams outcropped conveniently on the sides of the valley and for most of the eighteenth century they could be mined via horizontal levels or adits. The coal was brought down to the wharves and works on wagon roads or rails. Some was carried colourfully in baskets on the heads of men, women and children, tipped into small wooden trucks and then trundled into the holds of waiting barges or ships. On the wharves and at the works it was probably the cheapest coal in Britain. Robert Morris in 1727 put it at one-third of the price of Flintshire coal and one-half the price of Lancashire coal. Cheap coal gave Swansea and the south Welsh smelters in general a huge advantage. Not only were new ventures attracted to the district but existing works were relocated. In 1792/3, William Roe & Co. moved to Neath Abbey on account of 'the scarcity and dearness of coal' in Liverpool, and in 1812 Pascoe Grenfell moved his works south from St Helens to take advantage of cheap Swansea coals.[27]

Like Neath, too, Swansea had a navigable river. The Tawe valley is narrower than the Nedd but, sheltered from the prevailing south-wester-lies by the peninsula of Gower and the promontory of Mumbles Head, it was easier for sailing ships to negotiate and less subject to silting. Small sea-going vessels could ascend the river for 2 or 3 miles; larger ones could anchor in the harbour at its mouth. For an industry dependent on bulk shipments of ore, these differences were crucial.[28]

First to take advantage of them was John Lane, a Bristol doctor and surgeon turned businessman and manufacturer. In 1717 he left his works at Neath Abbey to build the Llangyfelach works at Landore (Glandwr) on the Tawe 2 miles above Swansea. Lane rented the land from Thomas Popkin, an irascible and notoriously tight-fisted landowner who, as one of Neath's justices of the peace, had set the press gangs on Sir Humphrey Mackworth's workers. Ore for Lane's works came from Cornwall but its managers were never able to secure steady supplies. Even coal, which ought to have been cheap, Lane was forced to buy at high prices from the rapacious Thomas Popkin. Lane's tenure at Landore was brief. He invested in the South Sea venture, lost everything and declared bank-ruptcy whereupon his landlord, 'Old Popkin of Forest', as Robert Morris noted drily, 'lock'd up the Copper Works'.[29] It was eventually bought by a small group of Englishmen which included Edward Gibbon, grandfather of the historian, and Robert Morris, who managed the enterprise. From the outset Morris, who considered a copper works without smoke to be 'a melancholy sight', was determined to secure steady supplies of coal and ore. To do so he had first to put an end to Thomas Popkin's 'shifts' and 'tricks'. After the sale, Popkin had insisted on the terms of the orig-inal covenant, one of which prevented Morris from buying coal from other suppliers as long as Popkin could meet his demands. Supplying coal to copper works was so profitable that landowners clung to their mineral rights. 'I would have all who have money', Morris noted, 'to adventure in mining especially on their own estates.'[30] He was speaking from bitter experience. Thomas Popkin not only insisted on his monopoly but he used the advantage to supply only 'muck and dirty coal'. In order to mine his own coal, Morris leased a colliery from the far more amenable duke of Beaufort and on the river bank below it he built a new works (The Forest) which was a mere quarter of a mile from the old.[31] 'If only', Morris once sighed, 'Old Popkin would but die, or be good humoured.' To secure a supply of ore, Morris went to Cornwall where, confident that the advantage of having Tawe valley coal on his doorstep would more than offset the increased costs of the ore, he outbid the Cornish smelters.

Within three years of Dr Lane's move to Landore, in 1717, plans were afoot to build a copper works in Swansea itself. The proposal, made by a group of Quaker merchants and businessmen, caused a ripple of apprehension in the town. Although most of the smoke from Dr Lane's works had gone up the valley and across an uncultivated marsh, the people of Swansea had seen just how offensive and destructive it could be. Several of them objected to the building of a copper works within the town limits, but one of the backers of the project was the powerful Gabriel Powell, steward for the seigniories of Gower and Kilvey and portreeve of Swansea.[32] As both steward and portreeve, Powell, in effect, controlled the Corporation. Although he had invested in the project, Powell seems to have been less concerned with the loss of his own funds than with preventing, for want of some initiative from Swansea, all copper smelting from gravitating to Neath. He saw clearly Swansea's unique advantages for smelting copper and thought it 'very hard that the Inhabitants . . . should be debarred of seekeing those advantages wch their situation intitles them to'.[33] In the end, Powell's will prevailed. The Corporation granted the lease, declaring 'that the said work will prove very much to the advantage, and not in the least prejudicial to the Burrough of Swanzey or its inhabitants'.

Opposition to the new works had been incited by Thomas Popkin, that 'sad, litigious Man' – as Robert Morris had seen him – who must have regarded it as a threat to his Neath and Tawe valley interests. Popkin submitted to the Corporation that the health of the town would be damaged by the 'morbific' and 'deleterious' character of the smoke. Powell, however, suspected Popkin of motives that were less high-minded. In a letter to the duke of Beaufort, the seigneur of Gower and Kilvey, he wondered why Popkin, who had opposed Swansea's interests 'with all that lay in him', should 'all of a suddain' concern himself with the health of its inhabitants. He expressed his distaste for those 'whose avarice would ingrosse all advantages to themselves', adding that what gave him greatest uneasiness was that 'a cunning, crafty person (I mean Mr Popkin) . . . should prevayle with the Duke . . . to deny us a favour which tends to his grace's interests'. Powell pointed out that, unlike Popkin, he lived in Swansea and that he was unlikely to support an enterprise that might endanger the health of his family or diminish the value of his property. 'It was insinuated to me (who has been at 150 pounds abt my Garden) in order to divert me from this affayre that it would spoil my Garden – but that I look upon as idle as the least of their ptences.' He also pointed out that neither the people of Neath nor Landore had (up to 1717) complained of their respective copper works: 'There are several copper works near Neath, several inhabitants abt those works, and yet we do not hear the least complaint of any unhealthiness thereby.'

Powell kept his most telling argument till last. The site chosen for the proposed works, in the north-east corner of Swansea, ensured that the prevailing westerly winds would carry the smoke up the valley and away from the town:

> There is but one wind in the 24 and that wch blows ye most seldom, vizt. NNe, that will blow upon any pte of ye Towne, an ye worke being three fields distance from ye uppermost house in Towne I am wel satisfied it will not affect us.[34]

The argument was convincing and in 1720 Powell and his fellow Quakers built a copper works on the west bank of the Tawe just inside the boundary of the borough. Mismanaged, and unable to sustain supplies of either coal or ore, the works made very little copper, but it produced enough smoke – at times when the north-east wind was blowing – to shake the confidence of the Corporation.

Though Powell had been right to suspect Popkin's motives, he had misjudged the strength of the smoke. At Neath Abbey and Neath – until the building of the Melincryddan works immediately south of the town – the smoke had passed virtually unnoticed. The Nedd estuary is broad and flat and the valley itself relatively wide. Smoke from the Neath Abbey works sailed harmlessly over the estuary or drifted up the broad valley away from the town. The Tawe, on the other hand, was a smoke trap, concentrating the fumes. The valley is narrow and becomes even narrower toward the mouth as resistant sandstones replace the softer shales of the middle reaches. At Swansea itself the river, pinched between Kilvey Hill on the east and Town Hill on the west, flows through a gap barely half a mile wide. With the wind in the north smoke-laden air bore directly on the town. Although infrequent, the invasions gave the Corporation second thoughts about the benefits of copper smelting, at least within the town limits. When the copper works lease ran out, in 1764, the Corporation assigned the site to a pottery, the terms of its tenure expressly prohibiting copper smelting. Although there were already four copper works in the lower valley, with three more to follow before the end of the century, the Corporation had evidently decided that the town's fortunes did not lie in manufacturing.

The Brighton of Wales

No coastal town physically as well favoured as Swansea would, in the 1760s, have settled for coaling combined with a little trade and industry. With its southern exposure, magnificent bay, sands and, to the west, rich, attractive countryside, Swansea had all the attributes to become a major resort: the 'Brighton of Wales' according to one admirer.[35] Each summer, from the middle of the eighteenth century, Britain's middle classes headed for the sea. For a society without a scientifically based medicine, sea water, imbibed or merely bathed in, was the latest cure-all and people with means looked for pleasant coastal places in which they might spend the summers. As the incomparable Cowper put it:

> But now, alike, gay widow, virgin, wife,
> Ingenious to diversify dull life,
> In coaches, chaises, caravans, and hoys,
> Fly to the coast for daily, nightly joys,
> And all, impatient of dry land, agree
> With one consent to rush into the sea.[36]

To attract its share of summer migrants, the town set about improving its bathing facilities. John Morris of Clasemont sent to Weymouth for its best bathing machine and the Corporation hired a local wheelwright to make a copy of it. The Corporation also allocated £300 for an extension to the existing bathing house. By 1789 the *Guide to All the Watering and Sea Bathing Places* was able to announce that Swansea now had 'every accommodation for using the marine fluid with effect, in every possible way'. But as well as having their health improved or restored, visitors to seaside resorts expected to be entertained and edified. A bathing house alone was not enough. The Corporation built a suite of assembly rooms, supplied land for lodging houses, and made a Burrows walk on low-lying ground south of the town and adjacent to the harbour. It also furnished money for a band, a theatre, a newspaper (the *Cambrian*) and a subscription library: standard amenities for any town aspiring to be a first-class watering place.

As a resort Swansea never achieved the sophistication of Weymouth or Brighton, but the dream of elegance lasted well into the nineteenth century. Expectations may well have peaked in August 1802 when Lord Nelson (receiving the freedom of the town) and Lady Hamilton visited the Burrows and patronized the public baths. The excitement of the visit had scarcely subsided at the time of the Reverend John Evans's visit in 1804. He found that Swansea wished devoutly to be 'viewed in the light of a *fashionable* resort, rather than as a *trading* town; and a bathing place, rather than a sea-port'.[37] A proposal, in 1809, to erect a soap and candle works near the site of the former copper works alarmed Lewis Weston Dillwyn, the well-known naturalist and owner of the Cambrian Pottery. He had been assured 'by competent judges' that when the wind was in certain quarters it would affect even the Burrows, and prove 'highly injurious to the town as a *Watering Place*'.[38]

But whatever its social aspirations, Swansea and copper smelting were inseparable and no municipal ban could keep the smelters at bay. The effect of the ban, as Gabriel Powell could have predicted, was to send the copper works upriver where, as long as the works remained small and the winds steady, they were no threat to visitors and hotel owners. For a few decades, at the turn of the eighteenth and nineteenth centuries, Swansea was a town divided both in body and spirit. While its Corporation was ordering bathing machines, building parades and improving bathing facilities in the Burrows near the mouth of the river, a mile or two inland smelters from Cornwall, London, Bristol and Anglesey were building copper works. By 1800 nine had been built along the lower Tawe and the seven then operating produced the bulk of the fine copper ingots needed by the metal manufacturers of Birmingham, Bristol, Liverpool and London. Like it or not, Swansea had become the undisputed capital of the copper kingdom.

For about a century the kingdom prospered, producing riches for the coppermasters and, by the standards of the day, comfortable livings for their workers. Wars between Great Britain and America and Great Britain and France increased the demand for ordnance, driving up the price of copper and brass. In the 1760s the Royal Navy also discovered that a skin-tight wrapping of copper sheathing around the hull of a ship was a far more effective shield against the *teredo navalis*, a voracious wood-eating tropical worm, than double-planking and an intervening layer of hair, lime and tar.[39] A smooth metal surface was no more appealing to weeds and barnacles, so hulls – no longer leaky and mollusc-encrusted – could now glide through tropical waters. By 1780 virtually all British naval vessels were 'coppered'. Other navies with interests to promote or protect in tropical waters quickly followed suit so that by 1784 most French, Spanish and Dutch ships were also wrapped in copper supplied by Welsh works. A device that increased sailing speed and manœuvrability appealed just as much to the pursued as to the pursuers; by 1786, copper sheathing covered the hulls of almost half of the African slavers. But for law-abiding merchant vessels – 'constant traders' – in northern waters coppering was not as appealing; there was less danger from worms and in tidal harbours vessels had to be able to lie flat or 'take the ground'. Though malleable and tougher than lead, copper in thin sheets tears and holes easily. In 1832 pure copper was replaced by the tougher, and cheaper, 'yellow metal', a copper (60 per cent) and zinc (40 per cent) alloy patented by G. F. Muntz of Birmingham who conducted his research at Swansea's Upper Bank works between 1838 and 1842.[40]

To meet the growing market for copper, existing works in south Wales were expanded and new ones built. By 1850 copper smelting elsewhere in Britain had been eliminated except for small works in Anglesey,

Lancashire and Staffordshire. Virtually all of Britain's copper and more than half of the world's was refined in the small coastal arc between Pembrey in the west and Taibach in the east. Two-thirds of Britain's production alone came from the works crowded into the narrow valley of the Tawe. In 1860, the year of peak production, the few miles of the valley just above Swansea were home to 600 furnaces and a forest of chimneys. Except for Thomas Williams of Anglesey and Robert Morris – who had married Margaret Jenkins of Machynlleth – the smelters had neither Welsh nor Swansea connections. To begin smelting took capital – about £40,000 in 1800 – and neither Glamorgan nor Carmarthenshire could supply it in these amounts. Such wealth as there was lay in land and property and any surplus tended to go back into the estates. Investment in copper smelting came from two main sources: the mining interests, and the metal and brass trades.[41]

Manufacturers were keen to safeguard their supplies of metal while copper miners wanted a share of the profits that they supposed the smelters, in whose interests it was to buy cheap and sell dear, were making at their expense. Mining interests from Anglesey and Cornwall were the largest investors. In the 1780s the Parys Mine Co. and the related Stanley Co. of Anglesey began smelting respectively at Swansea's Upper Bank and Middle Bank works. Associated with both companies was the enormously powerful Thomas Williams, the 'Copper King'. When Thomas Williams died, in 1802, his son Owen managed Middle Bank in partnership with the Grenfells, a London-based Cornish family with interests in copper mining and merchant banking. In 1784 Pascoe Grenfell, as the head of a sales mission, had convinced the French Navy to buy for its warships sheathing and fittings produced by Thomas Williams's smelters. When the Williams family withdrew from smelting in 1825 the Grenfells, who took over both the Middle and Upper Bank works, dominated the industry on the east side of the Tawe valley until the 1890s.

Also from Cornwall came the Vivians, Swansea's other copper-smelting dynasty. In 1800 John Vivian, who had extensive mining interests in Cornwall began moving his capital into smelting. He acquired a share in the Cheadle Co's copper works at Penclawdd on the Llwchwr estuary but, judging the estuary to be too shallow for safe shipping and too far from sources of coal, he began the search for a new site.[42] In 1809 he took a lease, in the names of his two sons, on a tract of flat land on the west bank of the Tawe just above Swansea. The land lay at Hafod, then a place of – in the words of an anonymous eighteenth-century poet – 'verdant fields' and 'purer air'. John Vivian's works at Hafod became a model for the industry and his son John Henry Vivian and grandson

Henry Hussey Vivian, who directed the works, were the acknowledged leaders of the copper trade in Britain and indeed the world.

On the manufacturing side, investment came from the metalworking centres: Birmingham, Bristol and London. Early investors were copper and brass manufacturers from Snow Hill, London, who in association with the London merchant Chauncey Townsend built the Upper Bank works in the mid-1750s. Townsend seems to have become involved in smelting to ensure a steady demand for coal from Tawe valley mines in which he had invested, but for brass and copper manufacturers the incentive was a guaranteed supply of metal. The White Rock works, for example, might well have been built (c.1736) 'out of Pique' by the Bristol manufacturer Joseph Percival because Robert Morris refused to sell him refined copper.[43] Truly threatening to metal manufacturing interests was the power of Thomas Williams. Not only did he control the production of the Anglesey and – from 1787 to 1792 – the Cornish mines, but he also owned smelters in Amlwch and St Helens as well as Swansea.[44] To offset the threat posed by Williams's monopoly, in the 1790s three Birmingham companies operated smelters in Tawe valley. Two of these, the Birmingham Mining & Copper Co. and the Rose Copper Co., were co-operative ventures producing refined metal for their members. A heavy investor in the Rose Co. was Matthew Boulton, of steam engine fame, who in 1797 had secured government contracts for copper coinage.

Eighteenth-century copper works were small affairs employing usually between thirty and seventy men. Early in the nineteenth century the scale changed. John Vivian's business strategy was to smelt to full capacity and sell as cheaply as necessary. Hafod from the outset employed 300 men. But its reign as Swansea's largest works ended in 1834 when two families, named Williams and Foster, with mining, banking and trading interests in Cornwall and London, built the giant Morfa works. To operate Morfa required the labour of more than 600 men. Though neighbours, Morfa and Hafod were locked in competition and divided by a great stone wall.[45] They were also divided by a wall of secrecy. The employees of both works were sworn never to disclose the secrets of smelting to anyone but their children.

Compared with the labour-intensive iron industry, the copper industry was not a large employer in spite of a few giant works. Yet by the 1820s Swansea works alone employed more than 1,000 men and supported, counting the collieries and shipping dependent on them, a population of eight to ten times that number. Tourism could hardly compete with this, so Swansea slipped the reins of fashion and reluctantly donned the heavier harness of industry and trade. One of the first public admissions of the town's changed role was an editorial in the *Cambrian* written, in 1822, in response to a complaint about copper smoke. While regretting the nuisance caused by the smoke, the editor acknowledged that Swansea, Neath and Llanelli lived by their smelters and affirmed that if it came to a choice between copper works or smoke-free air 'we hesitate not to say [that we would] endeavour contentedly to bear the annoyance of the smoke'.[46]

2

Shipping and the Ports

ॐ

The copper works at the mouth of the Llwchwr and around Swansea Bay were great maws that consumed enormous quantities of coal and copper ore. To make a ton of metal at the beginning of the nineteenth century required about 30 tons of coal and 12 of ore. When Edward Donovan visited the Taibach works in 1804 he commented upon the 'amazing quantity' of coal consumed.[1] The country around the works was seamed with wagon roads, tram roads, and canals that funnelled coal from the mines to the calciners and smelters along the rivers and the coast. All the ore came by sea, in small coastal vessels at first, from mines in Cornwall, Cardigan, Anglesey and County Wicklow in Ireland. During sailing weather, harbours and river mouths at Neath, Taibach, Llanelli and Swansea were alive with vessels delivering ore and loading coal. When Edward Donovan asked for a room at the Taibach Inn the landlord chided him gently for not realizing that in a small town of miners and smelters the house would always be 'crowded with captains of vessels, and their mates, whose business brings them to the copper works'.[2]

Until the 1820s mines in Britain had been able to supply the needs of south Welsh smelters, but as the demand for ore grew, Cornish, Welsh and Irish mines were unable to satisfy it. Production from British mines increased until the middle of the century but never to the levels required, and as poorer lodes and veins were exploited the quality of the ore deteriorated. As a result, copper ore had to be imported. First to arrive were Australian ores, at Hafod in 1827, followed by ores from Spain, Cuba and South America. Prospecting in the Chilean and Peruvian Andes quickened with the ending of Spanish rule in 1824, and by the 1830s Chileans, with the help of British capital and expertise, were exporting ore to Swansea.[3] By the middle of the century, when Chilean mines came into full production, 'copper-ore Cape Horners' of 300–1,000 tons were plying the sea lanes of the Atlantic and the Pacific. Swansea, by far the largest importer of copper ore, had a 'splendid' fleet of about 150 sailing ships all bent on the same errand: 'coal out and copper home'. Inward-bound ships carried ore; outward-bound carried coal to the ore-producing countries.

Tidal Estuaries

At all the ports, facilities for unloading ore and loading coal were crude. The estuaries were shallow and tidal, and none had adequate harbours and docks. The 'shipping place' at Taibach was an unprotected quay on a shallow, twisting estuary – the Old Bar – which served both the Afan and the Ffrwdwyllt rivers.[4] Conditions were even more difficult at Penclawdd and Llanelli. Open to the westerlies, and roiled by strong tidal flows, the Burry estuary was a treacherous waterway of shifting mudbanks and narrow, serpentine passages. As at Taibach, coal and ore were loaded and unloaded at small quays or wharves in partially sheltered inlets or pills. At low tide the vessels lay on the mud or sand.

Utterly dependent on shipping for the delivery of ore and – until the development of railways – the dispatch of metal, all the coppermasters were concerned about 'navigation'. On their arrival at Llanelli in 1804, Charles Nevill and his son Richard Janion Nevill, founders of the Llanelli Copper Co., addressed the problems of shipping.[5] They raised funds for a survey of the Burry estuary, and for the purchase of buoys to mark the main channels to Llanelli and Penclawdd. Incensed by what they regarded as a newcomer's interference with 'the rights of the shore', local smugglers, wreckers and beachcombers removed them. Not to be thwarted, Charles Nevill had the buoys replaced and, to the fury of the wreckers and beachbombers, he made the approaches even safer by providing a pilot skiff, manned around the clock, to bring incoming vessels safely ashore. To protect ships in the the harbour from heavy swells that jostled and scraped the vessels when they were tied to the wharves, the Nevills and the Llanelli mine owners extended the breakwater at the mouth of the harbour. Their finest work, however, was the new Copperhouse dock, built in 1825. Equipped with sluice gates to impound water, the new dock was a 'float', oblivious to tides, in which vessels could be loaded or unloaded at any time of the day or night. For the first time in a Welsh port, vessels at low tide were spared the indignity of having to 'take the ground'.[6]

The *Cambrian* hailed the building of the dock and the extensions to the breakwater as the final acts in the taming of 'a wild shoal and a dangerous shore', but others were sceptical. R. J. Nevill, in 1831, commented on how much more difficult it was to get vessels to load ore for Llanelli than for Swansea after the end of October. Engineers engaged to investigate the problem of silting in the main channel of the estuary between the breakwater and the docks questioned whether the problem of shifting sandbanks could ever be solved. H. K. Palmer, in an 1840 report, noted direly that 'the situation of the Harbour does not appear to have been suggested by any natural circumstance peculiarly favourable to such a purpose'. Seven years later Isambard Kingdom Brunel was just as damning, and far more direct. 'Nature', he thought, '[had] not done much to fit Llanelli for a Port.'[7]

Nature, too, had been niggardly at Taibach. To spare vessels the hazards of negotiating the shallows of the 'old bar', the English Copper Company and the landowner C. R. M. Talbot, in 1834, petitioned Parliament for a bill that would allow them to deepen and improve the harbour. By reopening an ancient geological channel, they proposed to give the combined waters of the Afan and the Ffrwdwyllt more direct access to the sea. The old channel would become a floating dock. The new dock, Port Talbot, lying between Aberafan and Taibach, opened in 1837.

A sandbar across the mouth of Swansea harbour, built from scourings from the Tawe, was also a hazard to ships entering or leaving. Only vessels with draughts shallow enough to negotiate the 9-foot high bar could enter or leave at will. Ships of any size either had to await the incoming flood tide or anchor in roadways outside the bar and be 'lightered', that is, have their cargoes unloaded into vessels small enough to negotiate the bar. Navigation had been an issue in the town since the middle of the eighteenth century when the growing traffic in copper and coal exposed not only the physical limitations of the harbour but also the executive powers of the private organizations then managing it. The Corporation viewed the harbour more as a source of income – from rentals, mooring and quayage dues – than as a vital town facility needing permanent upkeep.

At a town meeting called in 1768 to consider petitioning Parliament for a harbour bill, merchant and manufacturing interests met a wall of reaction. The portreeve, Gabriel Powell, who dominated the Corporation, opposed the motion. Unlike his father, who had welcomed the copper industry, the younger Powell opposed any development that threatened Swansea's autonomy. He warned that 'strangers and meddlers' would come into the 'poor town' and, by paving the way for an independent harbour authority, ultimately erode the powers of the Corporation.[8] Powell's towering opposition to the scheme, and a general uncertainty about traffic at the port being heavy enough to warrant major improvements, meant that the application was never made. The compromise, which satisfied no one, was to remove some of the 'paddocks' or banks of gravel and sand gathered in the river. Like all rivers flowing out of wet hills, the Tawe was subject to flooding and the deposition of sand and mud at its mouth. As a navigable river it was also subject to the dumping of ballast by irresponsible traders as they entered the harbour. Vessels forced, in the absence of a wet or floating dock, to lie at low tide on the river or harbour bottom also added to the unevenness. By preventing the free flow of silt-laden water a vessel lying in the stream made a niche or small dock for itself as sand and silt from the sluggish waters accumulated around its sides. At low tide the harbour bottom resembled the surface of a sand desert: a succession of hollows (pools) and whale-back paddocks on which newly arrived vessels usually rested unevenly. Long, large vessels in particular were liable to be 'hogged and much strained'.[9]

But dredging the bar and the harbour bottom, which seems to have been minimal, was no substitute for proper control and management. The question of a petition to Parliament arose again at a meeting of the Corporation in 1787. Powell, still the portreeve, reiterated the objections he had raised twenty years earlier. An Act of Parliament could only be 'very prejudicial' to the town and borough, and tend to the 'manifest destruction of many of [its] most valuable rights and privileges'.[10] Feelings at the meeting ran so high that Charles Collins, a determined proponent of harbour improvement, was knocked to the ground of the Common Hall and kicked. In the process he lost his wig and, to add insult to injury, he and his supporters also lost the day by ten votes to five.

For Powell, however, a harbour bill was only the thin end of a wedge that would open the door to government intervention. Outraged by a decision taken at a public meeting in 1786 to petition Parliament for a paving bill, Powell, then over eighty, travelled by coach to London to confront the appropriate Commons committee. The dramatic intervention, and his observation that 'Swansea is a poor town mostly inhabited by coppermen and colliers; but as well paved as most country towns are', caught the attention of the cartoonist Moses Harris. In 'The Steward', Powell is shown standing next to a dilapidated well in a filthy street that had become a pen for rooting pigs.[11] Like his father, Powell was steward of the seigniories of Gower and Kilvey. It was an ominous beginning for a town whose public health needs were, and would continue to be, greater than most.

Only after Powell's death, late in 1789, could the town petition for a bill to improve the harbour and the river. The ensuing Harbour Act of 1791 provided for a representative managing body, the Harbour Trust, made up initially of the Corporation, twelve burgesses and twelve nominees of the mining, manufacturing and shipping interests.

At first, little was achieved beyond the building of breakwaters at Swansea and a lighthouse at Mumbles. In 1794, the trustees commissioned a report from Joseph Huddart, a leading marine surveyor, but ignored most of his major recommendations. The channel was deepened and piers were built to inhibit silting, but nothing was done about the pressing need for a 'wet' or 'floating' harbour. Full powers to make a float by 'stopping up the water in the river' had been granted by the Harbour Act. In a subsequent report (1804), Huddart also advised the Corporation against leasing property on the west side of the river mouth, in the then fashionable Burrows, because he considered this to be the most suitable site for a second wet dock, should one be needed. The larger vessels needed for overseas trade would not, he thought, take the ground of the harbour either willingly or well.[12]

In spite of Huddart's advice, the example of Llanelli and the persistent demands of merchants and manufacturers, ships at Swansea continued to lie on the mud for another forty years. The most tireless advocate for a floating dock was John Henry Vivian who had been a harbour trustee since 1809. With help from the roadbuilder and engineer Thomas Telford he prepared, in 1826-7, detailed plans for a new floating dock, with upper and lower basins and a toll bridge to take traffic across the Tawe. But neither the existence of a plan nor – because of increases in the size and number of ships – the great need for a floating dock were sufficient to galvanize Vivian's fellow trustees. In 1832 they were finally presented with a plan they could accept, but it took three more years of painful discussion before they approached Parliament for powers to adopt it.

Yet neither parliamentary approval nor the urgent pealing of church bells that accompanied it could hurry the proceedings. Four more years passed before, in the spring of 1840, the first sod was turned for a new channel for the river: the New Cut. Work on making a float of the old channel, now an abandoned meander bend or oxbow, began in 1849 and ended in 1851. Within two months of the official opening of the new (North) Dock, on New Year's day 1852, the marquess of Worcester raised the first sod for a companion dock before a crowd of 80,000 people.[13] The site was in the fashionable Burrows. Swansea might have decided long since that its model for development would be Liverpool, not Brighton or Weymouth, but this was still a watershed victory for trade. When the South Dock was officially opened, on 23 September 1859, the *Cambrian* hailed the occasion as 'incomparably more important to us, as an industrial and commercial community, than any event that ever transpired in our midst'.

Copper-Ore Barques

A cargo as heavy and as bulky as copper ore required a vessel built for stamina not speed – a heavy horse as distinct from a thoroughbred. In the absence of a floating dock at Swansea it also needed a vessel that would 'sit well' on the mud of the harbour and withstand the 'working' of frames and planking in the strong tideways of the Bristol Channel. The thoroughbreds of the first half of the nineteenth century were the narrow-hulled racing schooners, designed for speed rather than capacity, that carried passengers, the mails and cargoes of low bulk and high value. Narrow-hulled or 'sharp-built' vessels could not take the ground and their owners would accept cargoes for Swansea only at a substantially increased freight. Cargoes were either lightered out in the Bay or unloaded at Liverpool and then ferried south in coasters.

The answer to the smelters' needs was the full-bodied, long-hulled barque driven by large, square sails on its main and fore masts. Barques were the bulk carriers, the 'floating warehouses' of the nineteenth century that brought sugar from Mauritius, grain from America, timber from the Baltic and palm oil from West Africa. Though slower than schooners and clippers the three-masted barques, which could still cut through heavy seas, were an acceptable compromise between speed and carrying capacity. A standard barque, weighing 300–500 tons, was manned by a captain, a bosun (often no second officer), a cook who often doubled as steward, a carpenter, eight to ten seamen and, very often, a ship's boy or apprentice.

At first the crews of the copper-ore barques were predomimantly Welsh, and rural rather than Swansea men. In Swansea, industrial wages were too high to make signing on attractive to any but the adventurous and the desperate, but in Gower, Carmarthensire and Cardiganshire, where there was never enough land or work to go around, young men looked to the sea. By the 1860s and 1870s, as both the number and the size of the barques increased, the masters and mates might still have been Welsh but the crews were international, seamen from Norway, Germany, Finland, England, Sweden and America invariably outnumbering the Welsh.

As a cargo, copper ore was one of the most difficult. When carried on the 'ceiling', or bottom, of the vessel its weight made for a very low centre of gravity and in heavy weather this placed a great strain on the masts and spars. Nor, because of the great weight of the ore, could holds be filled, so that in a rough sea the cargo could shift and endanger the ship. The solution, devised about 1840, was to contain the ore in tightly packed wooden compartments or 'trunks' that rested on a platform built over the keelsons, the longitudinal strengthening timbers laid across the ribs of the ship. The walls of the trunks, made from planked uprights that connected the keelsons and the deck beams, were 'tommed off' about 5 feet from the ship's side and, to prevent any movement of the ore, sloped inward toward the hatches. 'Swansea fitted' in shipping circles came to mean a barque equipped to carry copper ore. By containing the cargo and keeping it in the middle of the hold, the trunks raised the ship's centre of gravity, eased the strain on the masts and spars, and increased her stability. So critical were the trunks to the safety of the ship that in heavy seas the ship's carpenter crawled through the bilges to check that the trunks had not shifted or the ore come adrift.[14]

By keeping the ore away from the bottom, and the bilge water that inevitably gathered there, the trunks served another purpose vital to the safety of the barques. Chemically speaking, iron and copper are an excitable combination, and when the ore lay on the bottom of the hold the copper salts, leached out by bilge water, eroded the iron bolts that fastened the ship's planking.

Barques for the Chile and the Cuba trade were made in yards around the Bristol Channel – at Swansea itself, Bideford, Barnstaple and Llanelli – and in the Maritime Provinces of Canada. In the Maritimes, lumber and labour were cheaper than in Britain and, because of the thin population, sites for shipbuilding were far easier to find. To build a barque of a few hundred tons all that was needed was a sheltered beach or bank with deep water close inshore. Prince Edward Island's shelving beaches were the chief source of vessels and, with some help from New Brunswick and Quebec, the Island supplied more than half of Swansea's needs in the second half of the nineteenth century.[15]

One of the Island's leading shipbuilders was Swansea-born William Richards who as a young captain in the north Atlantic had taken people out and brought lumber home. On Prince Edward Island he met and married one of the daughters of James Yeo, a native of North Devon and one of the Island's largest shipowners and shipbuilders. In 1854 Richards acquired his first shipyard, at New Bideford on Richmond Bay, and by 1870 he owned yards in several parts of the Island as well as a sawmill and a large tract of timberland in New Brunswick.[16] To complete the Swansea link, William's brother, Thomas Picton Richards, was a shipowner and broker in Swansea. Between them, builder and broker kept up a steady flow of barques to Swansea; in 1858–90 the William Richards yards alone built more than ninety vessels, most of them for the British market.

Island barques were usually bought off the shelf, and for their maiden voyages they were filled with cargoes of oats and lumber, the latter for sale to the British building trades.[17] Masters, mates and experienced seamen were recruited in Britain, the Island's available labour being fully occupied in cutting and hauling timber and manning the shipyards. Incoming crews brought sails, ropes, rigging materials and even anchors but on leaving the Island the vessels were far from finished. Though the barques were strongly built, British sailors were inclined to dismiss them as 'patched together' or 'slop or cabbage stock built'.[18] On arrival at Swansea they were recaulked, given deck houses and, when necessary, had strengthening members built into the hull. As hardwood on the Island became scarce, spruce and pine were used for the lower timbers and these, if not well seasoned, were 'sappy'. But though more easily crushed and torn apart than hardwood vessels, 'Canadian softwoods' were unusually buoyant, a useful attribute in vessels designed to carry bulky cargoes. Lloyds registered Island vessels A1 for four to seven years against a ten- to thirteen-year listing for an oak-timbered and copper-fastened British vessel.[19] In an effort to raise the Lloyds classification Richards, in 1867, built the Island's first copper-bottomed (actually, yellow-metalled) barque. With the Lloyds inspector in mind, he was also the first Islander to build a barque under cover, the launch from the novel 'shed' attracting sightseers from distant towns and villages.[20]

Iron ships were also built for the copper-ore trade but, whether wind or steam driven, they were never popular. The first iron-hulled sailing vessel to round Cape Horn, the 550-ton *La Serena*, was built expressly for the Chilean ore trade in the Neath Abbey yards of Joseph Tregelles Price. Five years later, in 1853, the same yard built the luckless *Ellen Bates* whose uncemented bottom was so badly corroded by salts leached from her first cargo of ore that it had to be replaced.[21] The Tregelles Price yards also built some of the first steam-driven iron vessels, but steamships could make no headway in the copper trade. In the remote places where copper was mined bunkering stations were inadequate and the local coals unsuitable. Harbours, too, were usually primitive and turn-around times far too slow to make steamships economic. Swansea's copper-ore Cape Horners were the diehards of the age of sail.

Swansea in the Pacific

Cuban ores, mined at Cobre and shipped from Santiago de Cuba, were the first foreign ores to reach Swansea in any quantity. The Cobre mine had been opened by the Spanish and abandoned, presumably because of the diminishing quality of the ore, early in the eighteenth century. It was reopened in the 1830s when an Englishman, in Cuba to recover a mortgage debt held on a neighbouring property, had the presence of mind to assay some of the waste from the mine. It proved to be remarkably rich. When reopened, the now English-owned mine was worked by 200 Cornishmen but most suffered from fever and many died. They were replaced by *islenos* from the Canary Islands and Cuban labourers more than half of whom, at the time of David Turnbull's visit in 1838, were slaves.[22] The latter were the property of the mining company and of local landowners who contracted them out to the mine. At Cobre the ore was roughly separated from the gangue (stony or earthy material) by hand, stamped into granules by steam hammer and, after further sorting, loaded into bags or baskets for the 12-mile journey by mule or horse to Santiago. A standard load was two hundredweight. On his way to Cobre, Turnbull met or overtook some 400–500 mules and horses on their daily journeys to and from the port. The Cobre Company was reluctant to build a railway for fear that the veins of ore might end suddenly. At Swansea the company had its own wharf, the Cobre, in the North Dock.

But important as Cuban ores were, they were soon superseded by ores from the even richer Chilean mines. In Chile ore was not only abundant but unbelievably rich. When exporting began, copper contents ranged from 20 to 60 per cent compared with 6 to 8 per cent for Cornish ores and about 25 per cent for Cuban ores. Even the scoriae or slags, the wastes from rough Chilean efforts at smelting, might have had copper contents of 15 per cent. Later, when the rich surface deposits were exhausted, these were packed into sacks and taken to the coast.[23] For thirty years Chilean mines were the chief suppliers of the south Welsh smelters, making Coquimbo, La Serena, Antofagasta, Tocopilla, Carizal and Copiapo household names in Swansea. On a typical run, the barques called 'for orders' at Valparaiso – the organizing centre for the Chilean mining industry – and took on their ore, regulus or 'Chili bars' at one of the ports to the north. Regulus and Chili bars were concentrates of ores that had been roughly smelted in small blast furnaces. These used local charcoal at first, then coal from Wales to which inferior Chilean coals were sometimes added.

From Valparaiso, the closest mines were at Coquimbo and La Serena, two of the older mining centres a few days north. At Coquimbo there was a safe bay and a good anchorage and, between it and its neighbour La Serena, a fine sandy beach that the inhabitants used for swimming and promenades. The river Coquimbo, on which both towns stood, flowed through a fertile and well-cultivated valley. The people, as one Vivian agent noted, were 'very kind and hospital [sic]', and the climate 'glorious', allowing him to spend several months on the coast and in the interior without sleeping under a roof.[24] The people were also colourful. When down from the mines, Coquimbo miners wore long dark shirts, leather aprons, coloured waistbands and scarlet caps. In southern and central regions, the mines, too, were in attractive locations. There was very little smelting and therefore, as Darwin noted when ashore from the

Beagle in 1831, no smoke, furnaces or steam engines to destroy vegetation or disturb the quiet of the surrounding mountains. But about the business of copper mining in Chile there was nothing remotely colourful; the ore, in sacks or 'carpachos' weighing up to 200 lbs, was carried up ladders to the surface on the backs of straining labourers. Only when the mine was more than 600 feet deep were they allowed to rest on the way up. On reaching the surface the labourers were exhausted:

> their legs bowed, the muscles quivering, the perspiration streaming from their faces over their breasts, the nostrils distended, the corners of the mouth forcibly drawn back, & the expulsion of their breath most laborious ...
> After staggering to the pile of ore they empty the 'Carpacho'; – in two or three seconds recovering their breath, they wipe the sweat from their brows & apparently quite fresh descend the mine again at a quick pace.[25]

Conditions in the mines were described by Vivian Webber, a Swansea traveller who visited Charles Lambert's Bronse mine at Coquimbo in 1858.[26] Miners and visitors descended by a series of ladders, crossing the 'deep chasms' that divided the various parts of the mine by means of bridges of rickety planks. Miners laden with 200 lb sacks crossed these at a trot. Quoting an English resident of Coquimbo, Webber noted that the owner of the Bronse mine seldom paid medical bills. One false step and the luckless miner or ore carrier was 'dashed to atoms'. Miners worked stripped to the waist using a short, heavy hammer and a 'borer' or chisel to make the blasting-holes. The muscles of the hammer-wielding arm were 'enormously' developed, making the miners appear lopsided.[27]

At La Serena, when ashore on Sunday liberty, the crews from the barques might also have met Swansea men brought in to concentrate the Chilean ores. In 1842, Charles Lambert built coal-fired reverberatory furnaces at La Serena to make concentrates from ores rejected for their low – by Chilean standards – metal content (15–30 per cent). He also extracted the copper from metal-rich scoriae or slags discarded after earlier, inefficient efforts at concentration. By stamping and washing the scoriae the metal-rich parts could be separated, packed into sacks and taken to the coast. By 1852 Lambert was refining 'Chili bars' in a works he built at Port Tennant in Swansea. During an average year between 1854 and 1872, sixty coppermen left Britain for South America, many of them from south Wales. At the time of Darwin's visit to the Coquimbo mines the *major domo* was Don Joaquin Edwards, the young Chilean-born son of an expatriate – possibly Welsh – copperman who must have arrived in Chile shortly after the European discovery of the ores.

North of Coquimbo conditions quickly deteriorated. Vegetation thinned, the climate became drier and, in the far north, absolutely dry;

the Atacama is the only rainless desert. The coastline also became more formidable. For hundreds of miles a seemingly uninterrupted wall of brown, barren cliffs cast long shadows on the ocean. The ore ports, usually the only settlements, were shanty towns built along the base of the cliffs or, if there were breaks in the cliffs, around bays and at the mouths of valleys that were usually dry. Only rivers fed by Andean snows had any chance of reaching the Pacific. But whatever the location of the towns they carried the hallmarks of mining and frontier towns everywhere: unpaved streets, shoddy wooden or adobe buildings with galvanized iron roofs, bars, brothels, flies and – a Chilean specialty according to Charles Darwin – fleas.[28] Where there were furnaces for concentrating the ores, the towns and the general terrain were absolutely barren. The manager's house, the Casa Grande, might have had a garden, but all other vegetation would have been killed by copper smoke.[29]

For the crews at these northern ports, there were no pleasant sojourns ashore. Often there were no shipping places, the vessels anchoring in roadways offshore and being loaded and unloaded from lighters. To save money for the owners, loading and unloading were done by the crew. The coal was shovelled into one hundredweight sacks and then hoisted onto scales. Five sacks made a sling which was handwinched out of the hold and lowered into a lighter. It was miserable work, the dust and great heat reddening the eyes, scorching the hands and drying the throat. The work was also slow, in spite of twelve-hour shifts, and often made slower by irregularities in the supply of lighters. A discharge rate of 50 tons in a twelve-hour day was considered exceptional, so a cargo of 300–400 tons usually took two weeks to unload. As the vessel rose in the water, hands who were not unloading cleaned the hull and otherwise prepared the vessel for her return voyage.[30]

Although there were railways in Chile after 1850, most of the ore reached the coast on the backs of mules and donkeys. There was never enough co-operation between mine owners to finance a railway and, as in Cuba, seldom enough confidence in the longevity of the mines to make a railway seem worthwhile. For the mules forced to negotiate the rough tracks the standard load was two hundredweight, packed in leather bags, and fastened with thongs to the often bleeding backs of the ill-used, half-starved animals. The mule trains were usually led by an old mare, a *madrina*, from whose neck a bell was hung. Virtually every track taken by the trains was littered with the carcases of animals felled by a combination of exhaustion, hunger and thirst. Darwin, ashore from the *Beagle* in southern Peru in 1831, described the scene thus: 'A complete and utter desert. The road was strewn with the bones and dried skins of the many beasts of burden which had perished from fatigue.'

Fodder, which could be grown only along the banks of the few permanent streams, was always at a premium: 'the whole value' of the Chilean copper-mining industry, Darwin noted wryly, depended upon a supply of pasturage. At Copiapo he visited the estate of Mr Bingley, an Englishman engaged in mining and exporting copper ore, whose entire estate – a green ribbon along the river two fields wide and 25 miles long – was devoted entirely to the growth of clover.[31] So scarce was forage that on their journeys to the coast mules were diverted through irrigated valleys; periodically, too, they were taken to pastures in the Andean foothills, a manœuvre that brought traffic to a standstill. Only when dried and pressed lucerne grasses were brought in from the south, in the 1870s, could mules head directly for the coast.[32]

Loading the ore, especially if it had to be lightered out to the barques, was also a slow, painful and – because the ore had to be tightly packed in the trunks so that it would not shift during the voyage – painstaking process. But when finished, the skies lifted at once. As the last load was hoisted over the rail it was customary for the ship's boy, or the youngest member of the crew, to jump onto the sling. He was then raised high enough for the ships around to see, and at the top of his voice he called for three cheers for the captain and crew of his vessel. That evening at eight o'clock the 'homeward bounder' started to ring her bell; neighbouring ships joined in and for about fifteen minutes the harbour or roadstead echoed to a chorus of bells and cheers. A wooden frame hung with five lighted hurricane lanterns in the form of the Southern Cross was hoisted at the foremast and, if tradition was followed to the end, before the hands turned in everyone aboard joined in the singing of the 'Homeward Bound' shanty:

> O fare you well, I wish you well!
> Good-bye, fare you well; goodbye, fare you well!
> O, fare you well, my bonny young girls!
> Hoorah, my boys, we're homeward bound!

The Voyage

Of all commercial voyages, the run from Swansea to Chile and back in ships heavy with copper ore, coal (and sometimes firebricks and fireclay) was considered the most testing. Apart from occasional sightings when rounding Cape Horn, there was no landfall until Valparaiso (where forwarding instructions were usually semaphored from the shore) and no landing until arrival at the ore port. Both the Horn and the Doldrums had to be negotiated each way. The often stormy passage around the Horn has attracted most attention but the passage through the Doldrums, where to make headway meant taking advantage of 'light airs' and 'slants' of wind, could be just as testing. Ships without a breath of wind in their sails could roll clumsily for days in heavy swells that threatened to tumble everything overboard. The rain was heavy and sometimes continuous, the heat suffocating and the haze enveloping. Crews, forced to handle ropes that were constantly wet, suffered from softened and split hands.[33]

On average, a round trip of 14,000–16,000 miles took from six to nine months. The record run from Swansea to Valparaiso was made in sixty-eight days, and many vessels completed the voyage in seventy to seventy-five days, but when barques could not 'make westing' around the Horn voyages of 150 days or more were not unheard of. With prevailing winds from the west or north-west and a current running continuously east, making enough headway to clear the land and then run north up the Chilean coast was no simple matter. Progress depended on changing the tack to take advantage of sudden wind shifts to the south and south-west, but if the tack was too slow a ship heading toward the south-west could be caught with her sails aback and be driven stern-first against the sea. The penalty for missing the tack was usually swamping or dismasting. In 1879 the iron barque *Kate Helena*, laden with 630 tons of coal and fire bricks, took six weeks to round the Horn and then had to be abandoned when a Pacific hurricane ripped out the main and mizzen masts. 'Unmanageable owing to stress of weather', the stock phrase used to justify the abandoning of a ship, scarcely touches the drama and the danger.

On ships poorly victualled to begin with, protracted voyages meant that crews would be reduced to iron rations long before landing. The reduction was from a staple diet of salt pork or beef, and biscuits (Liverpool 'pantiles') so impervious to teeth that they sometimes had to be broken with a hammer wrapped in cloth and the pieces softened in warm soup. There was no butter or fat of any kind, no potatoes and in rough seas, with the galley flooded much of the time, no hot food. Most owners and masters were so penny-pinching that the men had to provide their own knives, forks and spoons.[34] If, as on the *Cornwall*, the cook was a laudanum addict and an alcoholic then the food was probably inedible. When only a few days out of Swansea the master of the *Cornwall*, Frederick Watkins, found the cook – who was also acting as steward – to be 'drowsy and stupid [and] not in the least comprehending what he is about'. For the remainder of the voyage he was forgiven his duties as steward and confined to the galley.[35]

The outward passage, when barques rounding the Horn had to beat into the westerlies, was usually the most difficult, but the homeward passage

rounding the Horn in thick and dirty weather in 1872 Captain Edwin Jones of the *Herradura* had to reproach his chief mate for conducting his watch always on the lee side of the poop in the shelter of one of the boats.[43] Just as reprehensible, if judged by the unforgiving code of the sea, was the hand on the *Caldera* who, also in 1872, refused to take his watch because he was cold and wet and had been unable to sleep.[44]

Whatever their failings, Swansea seamen were tireless in their pursuit of copper. Even tenacious Yankee sailors acknowledged their superiority. If there was copper to be had in any part of the world, Yankees used to say, it was no use going there because you would be sure to find a Swansea man had already 'backed his cart in'. At times Swansea ships, which carried nitrates, phosphates and guano as well as copper, were so thick off the coasts of Chile and Peru that competitors were wont to ask if Swansea 'owned' the Pacific. Swansea men, or men employed by south Welsh smelters, were also active ashore, finding, assaying and purchasing supplies of ore. In the mining districts they moved from port to port, being paid a bonus for every ton of ore shipped over an agreed amount.[45]

Yellow Fever in Swansea

Yet for all their resilience not even Swansea sailors were proof against the nineteenth-century mariner's greatest enemy: disease. Deaths from disease and accident were common enough that 'No Deaths' was a standard caption in newspaper shipping reports. Scurvy was a perennial hazard because of inadequate diets and failure to drink the full 'whack' of lime juice. But more feared than scurvy, which was preventable, were tropical diseases. These could decimate a crew and in rough weather render a vessel helpless. In January 1845, the brig *Appleton*, a Cuba trader whose crew was too ill or too exhausted to man her, was saved only through the brave intervention of John Walker, a Swansea pilot. In heavy seas in the channel, Walker boarded the anchored *Appleton*, cut the anchor rope and brought the vessel into Swansea. But as tombstones in churchyards on the Gower coast still attest, other ships were lost because crews were too diminished or too weak to withstand the gales that frequently swept the western approaches.

The *Appleton* was only one of a dozen ships arriving, in January 1845, with ore from Cuba. The *Cambrian* noted each arrival and reported, ominously, that mortality rates were unusually high. Each vessel had lost at least one of her crew, and one of them, the *Lady Pirie*, five or six. The Cambrian ascribed the deaths to 'the fatal influences of that [the Cuban] climate'. The deaths, however, had nothing to do with the Cuban climate as such. The deadly infections were spawned not, as was generally thought, by fetid air but by the mosquito *Aedas aegypti*. The disease was the dreaded yellow fever, or 'Yellow Jack' as it was known to sailors, and it killed enough sailors in Cuba for Santiago de Cuba to be dubbed the 'Swansea cemetery'. Its dreaded symptoms were burning temperatures, severe shivering and pains, prolonged bouts of vomiting and a yellow staining of the skin. Cooks and stewards working in hot galleys seem to have been particularly vulnerable to the disease and in the Cuban ports it was sometimes necessary to replace them with native Cubans.

Though sickness and death were frequent visitors to the ore barques, shipboard diseases seldom ventured ashore and yellow fever or Yellow Jack, as far as was known, never, although there were suspected cases involving sailors, pilots and a ship's watchman in 1843, 1851 and 1864.[46] All changed in 1865. On 8 September of that year, during a spell of exceptionally hot, dry weather (70° F–80° F), the wooden sailing ship *Hecla* with a cargo of copper ore from Santiago de Cuba showed her light at Mumbles Head, off Swansea. The ship's boy, George Wilson, had died of yellow fever in Cuba and an able seaman, Hans Pedersen, had been left in a Santiago hospital 'sick of fever'. Three more crew members died on the homeward voyage and a fourth was said to be sick with dropsy. No fever was reported, and the unsuspecting pilot and the five supplementary crew members requested by the master, William Clouston, brought the *Hecla* into the North Dock, in the heart of the town.[47]

Showing no fever flag, the *Hecla* tied up at the Cobre wharf and within the hour her crew and the two passengers on board had disembarked, taking their belongings with them. The sick man, James Saunders, was taken to a filthy hovel, Welcome Court, just off the Strand and there visited by two physicians. One of them, familiar with shipboard diseases and the dreaded black vomit, *vomito negro*, diagnosed 'fever, probably yellow fever'. Official alarm bells now began to ring. Saunders was visited by a third physician and the mayor, J. Clarke Richardson, who doubled as chairman of the local board of health. At the time Swansea had no medical officer of health. Clarke Richardson had just left the premises when a message reached him that the sick man had died. Within hours Saunders's body, wrapped in a tarred sheet, was buried and the houses of Welcome Court were emptied and their rooms disinfected with chloride of lime.

Good sense demanded the immediate removal of the *Hecla*, but British law allowed of no direct assault on the vessel. Unloading had already begun and the Swansea agent for the Cobre Mining Association, the owners of the vessel, rejected all appeals to move on grounds that it would delay the return of the vessel to Cuba. He also pointed out that in thirty years no ship from Cuba had infected the town even though several were suspected of carrying yellow fever. His argument rested on the widely held assumption that epidemic diseases were spread not by the transfer – through the air or from person to person – of infectious material, but through random contact with pockets or layers of air charged with poisons or miasmas.[48] Pasteur's germ theory was still several years away. In its 1849 report the General Board of Health leaned heavily against quarantine on the grounds that epidemic diseases had their 'primary and essential condition' in an 'epidemic atmosphere'. There was little evidence to suggest that quarantining worked and for a maritime nation so dependent on trade the strict enforcement of an unproven system was seen as unduly punitive. The *Hecla*, according to conventional medical wisdom, had been unlucky enough to pass through a layer of atmosphere charged with yellow-fever poison.

Unable to remove the offending vessel, town and harbour authorities adopted the only measure left to them – they isolated it. Town police ordered the evacuation of the vessel and refused to let others go aboard. With unloading suspended, and the Cobre Co. agent suddenly a good deal more co-operative, the hatches were closed and the barque swabbed with chlorine and chloride of lime and then fumigated. Unloading began again on 13 September and when finished the discharged ore, sprinkled with Burnett's fluid, a chlorine solution, was left on the quayside.

On 15 September the epidemic began. A man who had worked on the barque came down with a severe headache, high fever, delirium and frequent vomiting. Although he recovered, he remained 'much jaundiced'. Others who showed the same symptoms were not as lucky. Out of twenty-two cases diagnosed as yellow fever fifteen died, all within a matter of weeks of the diagnosis. Six other cases were suspected and of these one died. Of the twenty-two confirmed cases of fever, eleven were inhabitants of the 'little island' between the North Dock and the Tawe; among the dead were ore carriers, an ore assayer, a blacksmith and a harbour patrolman. Of the remaining victims only two, who lived across the dock within 150 yards of the ship, had no direct connection with the island or the Cobre wharf.

Two of the deaths occurred at Llanelli, and these might never have happened had ocean-going vessels been able to negotiate the serpentine channels of the Burry estuary. On 22 September the sloop *Eleanor* arrived at Llanelli, having just discharged her cargo of copper ore at Penclawdd. She had sailed from Swansea a few days earlier. Within a week three members of her crew came down with fever and two died subsequently. While loading ore in the North Dock, for transhipment to Penclawdd, the

Eleanor had lain between the *Hecla* and the wharf. A few days later, on the 24 or 25 September, the *Hecla* was moved to the Beaufort Dock, a secluded inlet off the North Dock and the next day, following threats of burning by angry townsfolk, to a jetty in the outer harbour.

Not until the beginning of this century could the anomaly of the *Hecla* be explained. Yellow fever is a mosquito-borne disease and its vector, *Aedes aegypti*, requires tropical conditions in which to live and breed. During her voyage across the Atlantic, which began on 26 July, the *Hecla* was south of the 70° F isotherm for about a third of the time and south of the 60° F isotherm all of the time. At Swansea itself conditions were near-tropical: daytime temperatures were above 70° F for most of September and relative humidity was around 80 per cent. Although George Buchanan, a medical officer for the Privy Council, knew nothing of mosquito vectors he noted in his report that a low-lying alluvial island (between the North Dock and the Tawe) during an unusually hot spell simulated tropical conditions.[49] Aboard the *Hecla* conditions were favourable for breeding. The *Aedes aegypti* breeds chiefly in shaded pools and tanks and until the days of steam and piped water the water containers on sailing vessels were ideal breeding grounds. And once hatched, the mosquitoes discovered that the dark corners of the hold were a more than satisfactory resting place between blood feeds. On copper ore barques the *Aedes aegypti* seldom survived the passage across the cool north Atlantic but in the unseasonably hot September of 1865 the opening of the hatches and the unloading of the ore loosed a deadly vector on the luckless residents of the North Dock.[50]

Although death and disease were frequent visitors to the ore barques, vessels did return with their crews healthy and intact. In such cases the homecomings were often joyful. Frequently the ships, held up by the bar across the estuary, would be towed into the harbour six or seven at a time on the incoming tide. Friends and relatives gathered around the dockside and, as the vessels approached the dock the crews, in good heart, might have sung a verse or two of the rousing shanty 'Old Swansea Town Once More':

> Goodbye my lovely Nancy
> Ten thousand times adieu
> I'm going away for to leave you,
> Once more to part from you,
> Once more to part from you, fine girls
> You are the girls we adore,
> But still we live in hope to see,
> Old Swansea Town once more, fine girls.

Now our storms are over,
And we are safe on shore;
We will drink success to all the girls,
And the one that I adore.
We will drink strong wine and brandy, too
And we will make those taverns roar;
And when our money is spent and gone,
We'll go around Cape Horn for more, fine girls.

CHORUS
Old Swansea Town once more
And still we live in hope to see
Old Swansea Town once more.[51]

For stepping out on the Strand, a rich mixture of shops, workshops, inns, boarding houses, pubs, ships chandlers and sailmakers along the waterfront, sailors donned their best outfits. Nineteenth-century seamen took great pride in their appearance and Swansea Cape Horners, who were no ordinary mariners, were no exception. Dress uniform was blue dungarees, a clean jumper, a white cap, often with ornamental stitching, and small gold ear-rings. Once ashore they would join other 'homeward-bounders' in the inns and pubs of Swansea: captains in the George, bosuns and mates in the Cameron Hotel, and crews in the Cuba, the Cape Horner and the Mexico Fountain. The old Cuba, near the Strand, was usually the 'first drink' ashore and the 'last drink' before sailing.[52]

The Ticketings

Except for Cuban ores, which had their own wharf (the Cobre), copper ores arriving at Swansea were wheeled from the vessels onto common storage wharves, weighed and then registered. To prepare the ore for sale, the larger blocks were broken or 'bucked'. The 'buckers' were mostly Irish immigrants from Greenhill, or 'Little Ireland', the very poorest section of town, and among them were many women, girls and boys. Each bucker worked with a heavy hammer, or crusher, and a table on which to break up the larger lumps of ore. Inside the great iron-roofed storage wharves the scene was Hogarthian: dust, noise, great piles of ore, long lines of wheelbarrows and, as one witness wrote, 'queer geniuses of women, with short pipe in mouth . . . an old coat buttoned over their ordinary dress, begrimed with the yellowish green powder of the ore, looking like the inhabitants of some other world'.[53]

After bucking, the broken ore was screened, wheeled to its mother pile, then labelled. A wooden label, thrust into the pile, identified the quantity of ore, the vessel which had delivered it and the day on which it would be sold. Once labelled, or ticketed, the ore could then be tested for its metal content. At a signal from the wharf, chemists from the various works descended on the ore sheds and carried off samples of ore to their laboratories. Until the 1860s, when sale by private contract became more and more common, most of the ore was tendered for in ritualized assemblies, or 'ticketings', attended by representatives of the smelting and mining companies. The ticketing was a Cornish institution, dating from the 1720s.[54] The first Swansea ticketings were held in 1804 but not until 1815 were they a regular feature of town life. Held at first in the old Assembly Rooms, and then in the Mackworth Hotel, they were 'crack' affairs. Buyers and sellers were treated to an elaborate dinner, 'almost equal to a city feast', presided over by the principals of the mining companies. Dinner was followed by the ceremonial opening of the bids, or 'tickets'. Each ticket related to a specific parcel of ore and each buyer had to bid on all the parcels on offer at the ticketing. There were no reserve prices so no parcel of ore could be withdrawn. When all the bids had been opened, the president of the ticketing read aloud the offers made for each of the parcels. The winning bids, published in newspapers throughout the country, established the national and, in the 1840s and 1850s, the world price for copper.[55] A reporter for the *Morning Chronicle* who attended an 1850 ticketing remarked on the sedateness of the proceedings and on the total absence of that edge of excitement usually associated with large-scale buying and selling. The agents of the copper works sat at a long table, furnished with blotting paper, pens and ink, as though they were at a committee meeting and at the agreed hour tendered their folded tickets to the chairman.[56]

For the miners, the advantage of the ticketing system was that it guaranteed a sale with prompt payment. Even ores that the smelters could have done without were bought at the sales. But for this security the miners paid a heavy price. Although the ticketings preserved the trappings of a free market, prices were determined more often by agreement than competition. With smelting so heavily concentrated in south Wales, and mining – until the opening of Cuban and Chilean mines – in Cornwall, attempts to control prices through combination were inevitable. On balance, the smelters were far more successful than the mine owners. There were fewer of them – in any one mine there was usually a large number of investors – and whenever there was a surplus of ore the smelters collaborated over the bidding to drive down its price. Sooner than stop production, and run the risk of flooding the mines, the ore producers would sell at a loss, provided there was enough income to keep the mine open. When, as at Swansea, the shipments of ore tended to arrive in batches, the buyers had an additional advantage. At the early ticketings the Glamorgan and Bristol smelters were usually in such harmony over ore prices that the bidding was more of a duet than a duel, a finely orchestrated performance by the members of, as the mine owners dubbed them, the 'Old Company' or 'Associated Smelters'. But the mining interests were not always so indulgent. By refusing mining companies the power to reserve prices the smelters or 'Copper Lords', complained a disgruntled Cornishman, kept miners in a state that was little better than serfdom.[57]

At the Swansea ticketings, price-fixing was partly a matter of monopoly control and partly of collusion. The assayers of the smelting companies co-operated secretly to produce what was called the 'standard list' of the metal content of the ores on sale at the ticketings. The companies then decided on a price for each of the parcels and on the amount of ore to be allocated to each of the bidders. The size of the quota depended on the size of the company. Thus, at a ticketing in the 1840s, Williams, Foster & Co. was allocated 26 per cent of the ore, Vivian & Sons 22 per cent, Pascoe Grenfell & Sons 14 per cent. In 1837, R. J. Nevill of Llanelli commented that 'Messrs Vivian and Williams, Foster & Co. . . . by the system they now and for some time past have acted upon . . . are able to bring the Standard to whatever point they desire.' It all added up to what one observer described as the 'sweet simplicity' of copper broking at the Mackworth Arms.

The smelters also collaborated over the price of metal. A Copper Trade Association formed in 1824 and, made up largely of Swansea and Llanelli smelters, aimed at fixing prices in the main British and overseas markets. Rising demand meant that prices could usually be maintained without disagreement. The members also met periodically to settle tenders for the sale of copper to important customers, such as the Royal Mint, the Dutch Government and the East India Company.

After the ticketings at Swansea, the ore was barged upriver to the private wharves of the smelters, or carried in coastal vessels to wharves and docks at Penclawdd, Llanelli, Neath Abbey and Taibach. If still rough, the ore ran another gauntlet of hammers wielded by girls who carefully separated the ore from the gangue. From the wharves the now granulated ore was wheeled in carts and barrows into yards adjacent to the calciners and piled in ways that preserved the mix of ores advocated 300 years earlier by Ulrich Frosse. It was important to have mixes that were neither too earthy nor too sulphurous. Too much sulphur in the mix produced coarse metal and too little caused loss of metal in the slag.[58] To make doubly sure that ores from various sources were thoroughly mixed, the piles were cut vertically by the men who prepared it for the final few steps of its journey. The ore was loaded into one hundredweight boxes which were then lifted by water balance or, where there was no balance, hoisted onto strong shoulders and carried up to the sheet-iron hoppers suspended above the calcining or roasting furnaces.[59]

3

The Copper Works Towns

Crews arriving at any one of the ports around Swansea Bay would have encountered roughly similar arrangements of wharves, works, roads and houses. Behind the wharves lay the copper works and beyond these were their supply lines: the wagon roads, tram roads and canals that delivered an unending stream of coal to the hungry calcining and smelting furnaces. Furthest from the water were the houses of the colliers and copper workers, built usually on hill or valley sides, and sometimes following the line of a wagon road or tram road. Colliers and copper workers tended to live separately, copper workers near the works and colliers further upslope and – if the works lay at the mouth of a river – upstream.

As in most early industrial societies, housing and amenities tended to be something of an afterthought. Work came first, accommodation and comfort a distant second. In appearance, the copper works towns were little different from other industrial settlements. Communities grew around the works and most were little more than untidy collections of row houses, shops, chapels and pubs. On his visit to Taibach in 1804 Edward Donovan commented on the dirty appearance of the place and its inhabitants.[1] Hafod in 1840, according to one modern writer, was a rash of stone and slag-built houses, devouring the countryside: 'serried rows of back to back houses that eat their way through hedge and field, to climb and spread as best they may, unplanned, throughout the Vale. Hastily built, ugly, insanitary and overcrowded, these were the homes of the people.'[2]

Though unprepossessing, Hafod's rows were not as daunting as the battalions of company terraces in the mid-Glamorgan coal-mining valleys. On the western edge of the coalfield, demand for housing was never explosive so houses could usually be built piecemeal, a row at a time by the works, the mine or a private investor or developer. In the absence of standardizing by-laws they could even be picturesque. The 'Constant' (Constantinople Row) at Taibach, a long row of whitewashed cottages above the village, was for years a cheerful landmark for mariners entering the harbour.[3] At Swansea, J. T. Barber found that the whitened walls of the 'appendant' villages, that sprang from the dark sides of the Tawe, helped dispel the gloom cast by the 'manufactories' in the valley bottom.[4] And when Sophia Ward visited Swansea in 1791 she found that

> the lower class of people have better habitations – are better cloathed – and seem to live more comfortable than in other parts – their cottages are two storeys high covered with slate – and the fronts being all whited over – and the walls that enclose them – of the same colour – gives them a particular neat appearance – they have in general Geraniums at their windows.[5]

Neat, however, did not mean healthy or hygienic. In Swansea, as else-where, workers' houses were badly ventilated, innocent of running water and drains, and usually damp. If built below the surface of a road or a canal, or against a steep slope, back walls were often windowless and running with moisture. Gardens and backyards, where there were any, were no healthier. Each had a privy and a combined ash and rubbish heap accompanied by, in many cases, a pigsty and putrid casks of pig swill. All were convenient to the house. The compound of smells in the back-yards of Tawe valley villages, according to the physician James Rogers, was so 'villainous' that only liberal stokings of Franklen's pipe tobacco could fend it off.[6] Pigsties and rubbish heaps in the backyard were, in the main, expressions of a society careless of comfort and ignorant of the mechanisms of disease. But they were also to some extent the practices of country people who had recently adopted urban life; many of the copper workers and virtually all of the colliers were migrants from country places.

Morris Castle

Though products of a workful age, and staunch defenders of the rights of capital, the coppermasters were by no means Gradgrinds. Most tried to provide adequate housing and schooling for the families of their workers, and one of them, John Morris, even tried to create model communities. For his colliers and copper workers – he inherited the Forest works from his father, Robert Morris, in 1768 – there was little ready-made housing outside the slum disticts in the north and east ends of Swansea. To house Pembrokeshire colliers brought in, so it was said, to break a strike of local miners, Morris built not the usual row houses but a block of flats of, for the place and the circumstances, extraordinary elaboration.[7] Walter Davies, writing in 1814, described it as 'a kind of castellated, lofty mansion of a collegiate appearance with an interior quadrangle'. According to Davies it housed forty families, all colliers except for one tailor and one shoemaker who were considered 'useful appendages to the fraternity'. Although virtually nothing is known of the life of the community, Davies's use of 'fraternity' suggests that some degree of communal life was practised, or at least hoped for.[8]

The castellated look came from four corner towers capped with battlements made from blocks of copper slag. Each tower had a basement and three storeys of apartments, and each of the ranges connecting the towers, two storeys.[9] Except for a few string courses of copper slag blocks at the floor levels, the slag coping stones for the battlements, and a little brickwork, the building was made entirely of local sandstone. Diagonal chimney flues provided a form of central heating, each floor being heated from the floor below. Conventional heat came from fireplaces connected to a common flue. There was also a centralized system of rubbish disposal. Chutes placed alongside the windows of tenements in the upper storeys channelled refuse into a large collecting container.

In spite of conveniences which seem decidedly modern, 'Morris Castle' – as, inevitably, it was called – was not a success. Although they had gardens or potato patches, the miners, who were rural men, disliked living in apartments and they are not likely to have embraced the ideal of communal life. But the really insurmountable difficulties appear to have been physical rather than social or psychological. The Castle was built high above the valley on the crest of Craig Trewyddfa, ostensibly so that the workers might enjoy a view and breathe fresh, smoke-free air. Its location on a rock far above the water table and the spring line meant that it never managed to obtain an adequate water supply, and to enjoy the view and the fresh air the miners had to trudge up the side of the valley after a twelve-hour shift in the Pentre, Glyndu or Trewyddfa pits. John Morris may have thought he was serving his workers, but a Gothic Revival building in a romantic location suggests that it was more a landscape feature, balancing Clasemont House to the north, than a haven for miners.[10]

No one is quite sure for how long the building was occupied. It was put up for auction in 1811 and it may still have been occupied in 1850, but by 1880 it was in ruins. Quarrying around the base of the building brought down the two southern towers, and a recent storm one of the two remaining northern towers.

Morriston

The failings of his tenement building must have been apparent from the outset, but they did nothing to suppress John Morris's appetite for good works. His next scheme was more ambitious and far more practical. He referred to it briefly in a letter, written in 1819, to the then prime minister, Lord Liverpool:

> About forty years ago I appropriated a farm for the purpose of inducing the artificers and labourers of the County to build thereon giving them a long term of years, at a nominal acknowledgement with a sufficient plot laid on, for raising Potatoes. The scheme at the time was thought a visionary one, by all around me; but I have lived to see about 300 stone cottages with tiled Roofs, built by this class of persons.[11]

Although engagingly modest, Morris's description of the scheme is misleading. His design was for a model town, not just a collection of houses with large gardens.[12] To lay out a plan, he approached William Edwards, a well-known engineer and bridge builder who had superintended the construction of the Forest works. Edwards is best known for a beautiful arched bridge he built in Pontypridd, but he was also a celebrated preacher. Unlike the architect of Morris Castle, Edwards stuck to the low ground, both literally and metaphorically: he chose a conventional plan and laid out the town on a sloping terrace of green fields, just north of the Forest copper works, and near a mill stream, Nant Felin. The Tawe then was not only pastoral but it also had a reputation for good trout fishing.

Like most planners of new towns, Edwards settled on a grid, or rectangular pattern of streets. The plan's only distinguishing features were the spaciousness of the streets and the symbolic placement of a chapel-of-ease in the very heart of the town at the intersection of the two main streets. Instead of building the houses himself, the usual practice in philanthropic schemes of this kind, John Morris leased plots of land on very favourable terms to coppermen and colliers who could then build their own. The plots, of about a quarter of an acre each, were leased for fifty-year terms at 7s. 6d. a year.[13]

The houses, built according to a prescribed plan, had a central doorway, two storeys and a whitewashed front. Most faced the river and each had its own garden. The effect, which had been Morris's intent, was decidedly village-like. His aim was to provide his men with a link to the countryside, from which most of them had come, and he encouraged the steadiest of them to keep a cow on Trewyddfa common. Construction began in the 1790s and by 1796 there were 141 houses accommodating 619 people, a modest ratio for the time. Made from local stone and built by local masons, the houses, as Thomas Rees noted in 1815, were of 'a very excellent and commodious construction'. They also had good gardens and were, as Edward Williams (Iolo Morganwg) pointed out, 'detached from, but near to, each other'. Arranged along wide, straight streets, they represented a 'much more rational method of laying out a Town than has hitherto been adopted in this part of the world'.[14] Morris also endowed an Anglican chapel-of-ease and to preserve denominational balance – he was something of a latitudinarian – he provided land at nominal or 'peppercorn' rents for two chapels. He also introduced a form of workmen's compensation and set up funds to protect workers against sickness, injury and old age. At Morriston, and later at Sketty, in Swansea, he built houses for the poor.

Morris may not have set out to create an organized community, but this, in effect, was what he achieved. Of the original settlement only the street pattern and a handful of cottages have survived, but as one of the earliest examples of thoughtful town planning Morris's conception lives on. Yet however admirable the conception, the scheme failed in matters of practical detail. In his report to the General Board of Health, 1849, George T. Clark pointed out that the streets and roads were poorly made and no attempt was made to keep them clean.[15] Lighting and ventilation were no better than average and none of the houses had drains. Some, too, backed into the side of the valley and were damp as a result. Water was drawn from springs and shallow wells that were often contaminated with sewage.

John Morris might have been the only coppermaster to plan an entire community, but the provision of houses for the workers, or land on which to build them, was common practice in the industry. The Nevills at Llanelli, who may have taken a leaf from John Morris's book, provided building plots on long leases and at very moderate rents. The Vivians and the Grenfells, on the other hand, chose to rent houses rather than land. For workers at their Upper and Middle Bank works the Grenfells built more than eighty row houses, most of them on the slopes of Kilvey hill, and let them out at the standard rate of 6d. per room when it was said they could have charged 9d. and even 1s. 'in good times'. The houses were the usual two rooms up and two down with few amenities. But even without piped water and drains they are still said to have been a cut above the average.[16]

TreVivian

The Vivians, too, built large numbers of houses. At Taibach, where they bought the works of the English Copper Company in 1838, they eventually owned 130 cottages. At Hafod they built houses for key workers only at first, but by 1845 they owned sixty cottages in two streets. The rows were the nucleus of TreVivian. 'Eating' its way into the countryside, the community grew rapidly from these two initial terraces. Housing was mixed. The simplest houses were back to backs with two rooms up and two down, and grouped into terraces named after members of the Vivian family: Glynn, Graham, Odo and Vivian. The largest cottages had a parlour, a kitchen and a passage downstairs, and three rooms upstairs (one for the parents, one for the sons and one for the daughters) with windows made to open. Behind each house was a strip of garden with a privy, a pigsty and a coalhole, and in front a neat road and a pitched and flagged pavement. Rents were no higher than those charged elsewhere for filthy tenements.[17]

There was no water supply until 1850 – and then only for the larger houses – and no drains, but even so TreVivian was far in advance of the older villages in the valley. Pentrechwith, for example, on the north side of the valley was a village of old, damp, dirty houses niched into the hillside. Seepage from privies and rubbish heaps near the top of the hillside defiled springs near the bottom. George T. Clark had nothing but praise for TreVivian. He applauded the extensive use of cast slag in the walls of the buildings and – as coping stones – in the walls dividing the long gardens. Except for the lack of a water supply, he found it an exemplary development and recommended that it serve as a model for workers' housing in the district.[18]

But TreVivian's greatest admirer was Dr Thomas Williams, Swansea's most eminent physician:

> Grouped into streets and villages, ample in room, sound in structure, floored with dry bricks, roofed with tile and ceilinged, partitioned into convenient apartments, supplied with all the requirements of a civilized life, they [the houses of TreVivian] offer to the miner and the copper smelter . . . a home, attractive by its cleanliness, soothing by its comforts, and ennobling by its independence.

To 'breadless, homeless, tattered' immigrants from Tipperary or County Cork they offered conditions comparable with the 'palaces' of their native land. They were palaces, too, by the standards of miners' cottages in Pentre, Treboeth and Cwmbwrla. With cold, earth floors, unceilinged rooms, small windows and mud walls these represented, in Thomas Williams's phrase, 'the rude architecture of another age'.[19]

Of the other copper works communities, only Cwmafan attracted such extravagant praise. In 1845, a London journalist described the village as utopian.[20] A few years after selling its Taibach works to the Vivians, in 1839, the English Copper Company returned to the district and built a new works, just a few miles inland from the old, in the secluded Afan valley. To accommodate workers pouring into the valley from west Wales and the west of England they built several hundred houses, together with schools, shops, a market, a savings bank, a mechanics institute and a reading room which subscribed to more than twenty newspapers and journals.[21] The neat rows of two-storey houses, built back to back with room for a small yard and garden, are examples of well-intentioned, if mechanical, mid-nineteenth-century industrial planning. Nestled in a valley only three miles long and a mile wide, Cwmafan might have looked and felt utopian but it was, in effect, a company town. There was no elected mayor or council and until 1844 there was a company store. When, between 1848 and 1852, the English Copper Company was obliged to surrender its holdings to the Bank of England, the unpopular bank-appointed manager John Biddulph became, as a contemporary essayist noted, 'king of the valley'. The entire community lay under his authority – 'the works, the day schools, almost all the houses'.[22] He instructed the headmistress of the local school to discourage the use of Welsh and, a fanatic High Churchman, he insisted against a storm of protest that the workers' children attend the Anglican church. The children were threatened with caning if they failed to appear.[23]

Although concerned that their workers be properly housed, the coppermasters were not disinterested benefactors. The most effective way of attracting and holding on to workers was to provide them with land or housing at a reasonable cost. When building Hafod, John Henry Vivian remarked that without a house for the agent and a few cottages for the most valuable hands they would stand 'a bad chance of getting and keeping the best men at Swansea'. Because the works themselves demanded a heavy outlay, the coppermasters spent only as much on housing as was necessary, and they expected to get a return on their money. To recover their investment within a reasonable time, and pay for maintenance and repairs, the Vivians looked for a 12 per cent return on any houses they built.[24]

Copper Works Schools

Schools also fell within the patrimony of the coppermasters. Primary education was not a government responsibilty until 1870, and not compulsory until 1881. Before 1870 basic schooling was a matter of private enterprise, most often undertaken by churches, chapels and enlightened employers. At the opening of the Nevill Memorial Hall, Llanelli, in 1864, Richard Janion Nevill was commended for 'his zeal for the diffusion of education'. He helped establish a reading room and a mechanics institute, and between 1846 and 1848 he built, for the children of workers in copper and allied trades, schools that came to be regarded as some of the finest in Wales.[25]

Equally active were the Vivians in Swansea and Taibach. When the Vivians acquired the Taibach copper works in 1839 they took over a school, built by the English Copper Company in 1830, that was later described as one of the most outstanding in West Glamorgan and Carmarthenshire. Parents, however, were less enthusiastic than visitors and inspectors, many of them resenting the compulsory stoppage of wages (1s. 5d. weekly) and, in a monoglot community, the intolerance of Welsh.[26] The masters in general complained of the prevailing ignorance of English. In Swansea, John Henry Vivian subscribed liberally to the maintenance of the National (Church) School while his wife, formerly Sarah Jones, opened a small girls' school in Hafod in 1825 and converted the Swiss Cottage on their Singleton estate into a Model Dame School for twenty-five boys and girls.

Parents at Hafod are thought to have been lackadaisical about the education of their children, but the Vivians were not. Aside from their views about the general benefits of education, they were convinced that the key to industrial efficiency lay in a literate and numerate workforce. Possibly stirred by parliamentary demands for an inquiry into the state of education in Wales, between 1846 and 1848 the Vivians built schools and playgrounds for 600 children at Hafod. Children of their own employees attended free, others paid 2d. a week.

To choose a suitable mistress for their infants' school, John Henry and Hussey Vivian travelled to the Home and Colonial Institution in London to interview a woman trained in Pestalozzian methods. And to persuade her to forsake London for Swansea, they offered to build a house according to her design. In return for this beneficence, boys at the Vivian schools were expected to go into the Vivian works, while girls – after a spell at the works – were expected to fulfil what John Henry and Sarah Vivian regarded as their highest calling: good womanhood and motherhood. In the course of her long life, Sarah Vivian seldom failed to pay a weekly visit to the schools, and on 'Singleton Day' the children marched to the estate for a picnic and games in the field in front of the house.[27] In the 1880s, when Vivian power was no longer sovereign, the *Cambrian* referred to the occasion as a 'grandmotherly' gesture.

No less concerned about the education and general welfare of their employees were the Grenfells, owners of the Upper and Middle Bank works. But for them there would have been no schooling for children east of the Tawe in the early and middle years of the nineteenth century. The first Grenfell school was built in 1806 but it was a small and seemingly desultory affair run by an aged headmaster – a former mason – who complained that it was continually drained of pupils by the Grenfell works. In 1839 Pascoe Grenfell added an infants school for 200 pupils and in 1842 he divided the original (1806) school into a boys and girls section. When, about 1847, he learned that five young men who came looking for work had to make their marks, he determined that in future all Grenfell employees would be able to read and write.[28] He enlarged all three of the Kilvey schools and, provided there was room, he invited the children of non-company as well as company workers. Company children paid a penny a week, others slightly more. Although Pascoe Grenfell was a strong churchman the Kilvey schools, like the Hafod schools, were non-denominational. But where there was tolerance for religion, there was, as in Taibach, none for language. Literacy in nineteenth-century Swansea meant literacy in English. All books were in English and their contents had to be explained to the children in Welsh. Hussey Vivian allowed that Welsh might have 'poetic' interest but it was hardly the language of progress.[29]

As in the Vivian family, it was the women who took the keenest interest in the schools. Pascoe Grenfell had several reforming daughters who regarded good schools as the first step toward general social reform. Particularly solicitous was the remarkable Mary Grenfell who bought a prefabricated iron church and, disturbed by destructive drunkenness amongst the workers, opened a coffee 'tavern', the Golden Griffin, as an alternative to the beer houses.[30] The Vivians had also encouraged temperate behaviour by refusing to allow pubs on land or property owned by them. Although the coffee 'tavern' failed to empty the pubs of St Thomas and Foxhole, this and other Grenfell efforts at reform won the affection of the men.

Conditions at Work

Although well intentioned, the coppermasters were hardly sentimental. They paid the market price for labour and they expected value for money, from childen no less than adults. Boys of twelve were employed at Hafod and boys of nine at Taibach. Boys younger than nine were taken on only at the 'express wish' of their parents.[31] James Phillips, a fourteen-year-old respondent to the commission investigating the employment of children in 1841, had worked as a sheet-dryer at a copper mill for four years and before that as a pit-boy in Pembrokeshire. His work as a sheet-dryer was 'very wet and hot' and he was, so Commissioner Rhys William Jones noted, 'frequently much fatigued'.[32] The Reverend David Rees told the commissioner that the children at Taibach, who started work when they were about nine, were 'so weary that they had become indifferent about attending school'.

But for others work, however tiring, was a blessed release from the torments of pedagogy: George Williams, a twelve-year-old ash-pit cleaner at Taibach, had worked since he was eight despite his father's efforts to get him to attend school. 'I ran away', George told the commissioner, 'because I like cleaning the ash-pit better than learning the letters.' When families were large, wages low and schools tyrannical, 'mitching' (playing truant) was endemic.

At the works, the boys began by doing jobs considered to be light and unskilled, but these were still strenuous enough to cause frequent hernias. They cleaned ash-pits, greased wheels and machinery, wheeled coal and ore to the furnaces and, as 'cobbers', broke the slag to find copper for remelting. Others helped to pickle (clean), sort and shear the sheets of copper. Boys also kept an eye on the 'deadfires' in the furnaces during the 'long watch' from Saturday night to Monday morning when the works were closed.

The hours of work now seem appalling. In 1842 Owen Jones, a greaser aged twelve, worked up to fourteen hours a day with a ten-minute break for breakfast and a quarter of an hour for dinner. Under a strict foreman no other breaks were allowed. So that smelting processes would not be interrupted, twenty-four-hour shifts, 'long turns', followed by a day's rest, were standard for men and boys working at the furnaces. Usually they managed to sleep for a few hours during the night, in spells of about an hour, but this was not guaranteed. One boy who worked twenty-four-hour shifts as well as twelve-hour day shifts noted drily: 'None of us lie down during the night.'[33] It was said of John Henry Vivian that he could not bear the thought of letting out the fires at his works, and only in 1840 was he persuaded to allow his men to work twelve-hour shifts. Yet not all of them welcomed the change, some preferring to have every other day to themselves.

Women and girls also worked – but at the lighter and, in some cases, less savoury jobs. They broke the ore into manageable lumps, separated the ore from the gangue and wheeled both ore and coal to the calciners and furnaces.[34] In one nine-hour shift Elizabeth Matthew wheeled more than 20 tons of copper in 150 separate loads. Her shift, she confessed to the commissioner, left her 'far too tired' to attend evensong. Others collected urine from surrounding houses, carrying it to the works – where it was used to clean or 'pickle' the copper sheets – in narrow tubs resting on their heads. The practice persisted late into the nineteenth century. After the growth of a temperance movement, in the 1840s, young girls also supplied furnacemen with water 'specially selected', so one of the more circumspect owners claimed, 'for its purity'. During a shift a furnaceman usually drank between two and three gallons of water. At Port Tennant a girl, using a donkey, brought water from a fountain about half a mile from the works. Previously, furnacemen and refiners drank inferior beer and cider, supplied by the owners, and brought to the works in large pitchers by potboys.[35]

Most jobs at the works were taxing and uncomfortable, and some were dangerous. The air was always heavy with fume and dust and around the furnaces temperatures could reach levels that only hardened workers could withstand. Furnacemen, as R. H. Vivian remarked, needed 'the power of enduring ... great heat'.[36] When skimming off the slag with his heavy iron rabble or skimmer, a furnaceman – for fifteen or twenty minutes at a time – was exposed to the heat both of the molten metal inside the furnace and of the slag running off in a stream at his feet. To protect his leading arm, he often wore a piece of sail cloth covered with wet clay. Perspiration ran off him like rain, and the few clothes he wore became soaked. Only when clothes became, as the furnacemen put it, 'wringing wet with sweat', could they bear the heat of the fire. A copper-man commonly wore out four flannel shirts a year, compared with the collier's two.[37]

Yet almost unbearable heat was perhaps the least of the hazards. When J. T. Barber visited the White Rock works in 1802 he noted that condensing sulphurous vapour had yellowed the roof of the building and he suggested that if some method of collecting the 'noxious effluvia' could be devised it would 'save the health of the workmen, and spare the vegetation'.[38] All visitors to the works commented on the power of the fumes from the furnaces to, as one of them put it, overwhelm the uninitiated. But even the initiated could suffer. 'The men ... suffer greatly', noted another; 'they cover the mouth and nostrils with a handkerchief, and occasionally rush to a distance to inhale a less impure air.'[39]

In an essay on working conditions in the copper works about 1850, W. R. Lambert noted that when men from outside the district were hired by the copper works they either became used to the conditions or died within a few months. A pickler at the Morfa works confided: 'When I came here from the ironworks six years ago I suffered much from my stomach. The sulphur affected me. I spat blood for some time, but I became used to it.'[40] Isaac Davies of Hafod, aged fifteen, told Rhys William Jones, the investigating commissioner, that when he worked at the calciners the smoke and sulphur from the furnaces affected his chest and made him feel ill. Most boys, when starting work at the furnaces, suffered a temporary loss of voice. In an expression of medical honesty rare for the time and place, Dr Hopkin Llewelyn Pritchard remarked, in

1842, that respiratory diseases (chronic bronchitis and asthma) were endemic to Taibach copper workers. No wages, noted the Reverend J. Evans in 1803, could compensate 'for the great fatigue and unhealthiness of [such] employment'.

In addition to iron constitutions, men working 'before the furnace' needed presence of mind, and great strength and agility. The molten metal sometimes spilled and splashed, causing fearful injuries to the unlucky, the unwary or the leaden-footed. Reports of death and disfigurement from 'scalding' were all too frequent in the *Cambrian*. Even the smoke and fume could bring sudden death. In a thick smog 'which rendered the place very dark', Thomas Rees, a furnaceman at White Rock, missed his footing on a parapet-less bridge at the entrance to the works and fell to his death.[41] Furnacemen, too, could be felled by overheating and severe dehydration. In July 1811 the *Cambrian* reported that when fording the Tawe in a state of 'immoderate perspiration' copperman David Davies was seized with agonizing contractions of the whole muscular system that included a locked jaw. In hot weather, conditions at the works could be unbearable and both the Vivians and the Nevills complained of widespread defections. For men from the rural counties, the summer fields were sirens and few could resist the temptation to go off haying and harvesting. In September 1834 William Morgan, the works manager at Hafod, reported resignedly: 'miserable work . . . the weather has been close and warm . . . the men are indifferent about aiming at full work'. In May 1836 the Greenhill Fair caused a few more dead fires and that December, he noted, 'there never was such a drunken Christmas week and six or seven dead fires'.[42]

Some compensation for the fume, heat and dust were wages that tended to be higher and steadier than the wages of colliers and ironworkers. As a relatively scarce metal, copper fared well on the metal exchanges and the successive development of new copper products and new markets prevented recessions in the industry from being unduly long or deep. Labour, too, accounted for a comparatively small proportion of the total costs of smelting, so coppermasters were more inclined than other owners to yield to demands for higher wages and better conditions.[43] Supplements to wages were so habitual that Charles Nevill of Llanelli complained that the men demanded 'something for everything they do besides their wages'. The 1811 indenture of William Howell, a refiner at the Hafod works, entitled him to 'two pounds of Candles every Week and one Way of Coal every year and ten guineas every year in lieu of House and Garden'. For the wives of men who died while employed at their Hafod or Taibach works the Vivians provided a widow's pension.[44]

Despite the harshness of much of the work, coppermen were members of what E. J. Hobsbawm called the 'aristocracy of labour'. They might have been sallow-complexioned and 'dessicated, wiry, and thin', but they were well housed, well fed, well clothed and comparatively well paid. In his introduction to the first volume of the 'Blue Books', R. R. W. Lingen reported that when compared with their country cousins, the 'rude and primitive agriculturists', copper workers appeared to 'wanton in plenty'.[45] Only at Cwmafan was there a truck or company shop which, like all company stores, was closed by Act of Parliament in 1844. By forcing workers to buy from the company, truck shops – common in the iron industry – were a means of depressing real wages. On the industrial social scale copper workers were a full notch above colliers and iron workers. Their status showed, as one observer noted, in their 'content and comfort'. Strikes were 'a very rare occurrence indeed'. In the privileged world of copper, sons succeeded fathers, living out their lives 'without apprehension of change or discomforts arising from adverse times'. The skills of key workers, such as the refiners who performed the final stages of smelting, were usually passed on from father to son.

The quid pro quo for relative comfort and security was absolute loyalty to the company. Once recruited, skilled workers were tied to contracts that committed them to long periods of service, and to silence on all matters related to smelting and the business of the firm. William Howell, the refiner, bound himself to the Vivians for twenty-one years, solemnly swearing 'not to disclose [except to his own child or children] the Art or Mystery of Smelting or Refining of Copper as practised in the Hafod Works without the consent of John Henry Vivian or his partners'.[46] The contracts were no idle documents and the Vivians were determined to hold their employees to them. They took legal action against workers who broke the compact, and they once threatened to close the Taibach works if the sons of their employees continued to leave.

There were also occasional confrontations. As skilled workers, the coppermen had some bargaining power and the geographical concentration of the industry made combination possible. Requests for voluntary cuts in wages when markets were soft and prices low led to ill feeling and, occasionally, strikes. In 1820, a particularly troubled year, some of the Hafod men struck in May, and in August there was a 'great rising' of Grenfell's men. In the course of the dispute, John Henry Vivian complained of the 'riotous proceeedings' of the strikers.[47] There was also trouble in 1843 when a mass meeting in Swansea, attended by more than 1,000 coppermen, precipitated a region-wide strike. The men had suffered a 12 per cent cut in wages, the employers arguing that even after the cut coppermen's wages were still higher than those in other industries in the locality. At the Swansea meeting the Reverend Thomas Davies, minister of Pentre chapel, delivered an impromptu speech advising patience and loyalty. He reminded the men of the generosity of the masters when times were good and asked the men to return the favour in a time of depression. The men cheered the speech, which is said to have been 'electrical', and afterwards dispersed quietly.[48] But the effect of a speech that was more rhetorical than substantive was not lasting: the real grievances remained and a fortnight later the men struck at Hafod, White Rock and Middle Bank, and then at copper works in Neath and Briton Ferry.

In spite of defections, occasional confrontations and strikes, relations between coppermasters and coppermen were generally cordial until the last quarter of the nineteenth century when competition from smelters on the ore fields, rising wages and the growth of trade unions created tensions. Hussey Vivian alluded in 1862 to the 'long and peaceful connec-tion between master and men' and in 1874 he described the Hafod workers' enthusiastic reception of his election victory as 'the pleasantest thing of my life'. Loyalty may have been a contractual obligation, but it also seems to have been freely given. At best there was, to borrow a phrase from Grant Francis, 'a gentle feeling' between master and worker.[49] The workers at Middle Bank described the dying Pascoe Grenfell as 'our beloved master and friend' and after his death they helped pay for a memorial window in Kilvey church. During Grenfell's long management of Middle Bank, c.1844–79, there were no strikes or lock-outs. R. J. Nevill's death at Llanelli in 1856 also saddened the entire community and is said to have occasioned a funeral of 'enormous propor-tions'. But most revealing of all, perhaps, is a headstone in Mynydd Bach churchyard that reads: 'To the Memory of William Andrews, Copper Man of Vivian's Town, Nov. 21, 1856'. The deliberate wording suggests that William Andrews, as well as being a proud tradesman, was bound to Vivian by more than the terms of an indenture.

The World of the Coppermasters

When Edward Donovan visited Swansea early in the nineteenth century he noted that it was a town of striking contrasts. In the east was the port, the valley and the tightly packed copper communities; in the west were strag-gling villas, 'rising immediately to view', clean air and fine prospects.[50] Social position in Swansea was measured by distance west of the copper works. The southern and western parts of the town were protected from industrial smoke and smells not only by the direction of the prevailing winds but by the configuration of the lower reaches of the Tawe. High hills immediately west of the river deflected smoke-bearing north and north-east winds away from the populous parts of the town into the gorge-like valley. Swansea was far from being smoke-free but, as town and tourist guides were quick to point out, only on one day out of seven could even the most delicate of noses have detected anything offensive in the air.

At Swansea, the only coppermasters to breathe the same air as their employees were the Grenfells. In 1830, Pascoe Grenfell built Maesteg House just upwind of the Upper and Middle Bank works, and lived there until his death in 1879. Earlier, c.1772, Robert Morris had engaged the English architect John Johnson to build a Palladian-style house overlooking the Forest works in Morriston, but Morris made the mistake of locating it downwind of the works. When James Baker visited Clasemont in 1791 he noted that the smoke was so destructive of vegetation that places where the 'infection' fell with most force, were marked by 'absolute sterility'.[51] According to the lore of the district, Clasemont, a house that Baker found to be of 'modern and elegant plan', was dismantled in 1805 and the materials moved, 'all in one night', by hundreds of carts to Sketty Park, on the west side of Swansea. Clasemont may well have been dismantled but probably not – in what seems too neat a reversal of the 'tŷ unnos' legend – in one night and certainly not in 1805. Letters were written from Clasemont in 1819 and the house is shown in its original location on a map dated 1823.[52] But whatever the exact fate of Clasemont, the family did move to Sketty where they lived in a new house that commanded fine views of Swansea Bay and the surrounding countryside. The new house was designed by the Jersey architect William Jernegan, a former assistant to John Johnson.[53]

Other coppermasters were more circumspect than Robert Morris. Even the Vivians, who were as solicitous of their workers as any of their competitors, were careful to live well upwind of the works. When John Henry Vivian married Sarah Jones in 1816, he bought an existing villa, also designed by William Jernegan, on the coast road just west of the town and within an easy carriage ride of Hafod. The house, built in 1783, was 'a curious octagonal building', so shaped to take advantage of the fine views offered by all directions. It was called Marino for the most obvious of reasons. Vivian gave the house a more conventional shape by adding two small wings, but within twenty years he had it rebuilt in the style of a late medieval or early Tudor mansion house. Mock Tudor and Gothic buildings then were the height of fashion. The original house disappeared behind a Gothic facade of vertical windows and pointed arches, and beneath a thicket of Tudor turrets, pots and chimneys. There was also a change of name. In 1829 the Vivians bought an adjacent 42-acre farm owned by the Singletons and they promptly applied the old farm name to the new house. Marino became Singleton Abbey.[54]

To complete the transformation of Marino, John Henry Vivian commissioned P. F. Robinson, one of Britain's most popular designers of picturesque cottages and neo-Gothic mansions. Robinson's immediate aim was to sweep away the more functional buildings. First to go were Marino's stables and stable yard which obstructed the view from the front of the house. With the stables gone, Robinson noted, 'it [the house] commands all the much admired scenery of Swansea Bay from Mumbles point to St Donat's, with the coast of Somersetshire and Devonshire in the distance'. Where the stables had been he built a broad double terrace, laid out with flower gardens, that looked over wide lawns in front of the house.

On all sides of the house were ornamental trees and gardens, artfully arranged in the 'natural', English-landscape style. There were also fountains and statues, and an orangery and a conservatory, all necessary adjuncts to any fashionable house early in the nineteenth century. The new walls of the house were soon hidden by myrtles, jasmines, heliotrope, verbenas and other sweet-smelling plants that were then pouring into Britain from all corners of the world. Sarah Vivian was a gifted gardener and during her fifty years at Singleton she amassed a valuable collection of rare flowers and shrubs. Among them were early flowering magnolias and, those unmistakable badges of gentry housing in Wales, Himalayan rhododendrons. Sir William Hooker, Director of Kew Gardens, arranged for his son in Sikkim to send her seeds and plants so rare that they were to be entrusted only to 'the hands of those who will pay the best attention to their growth'. So rich was the collection that Singleton's gardens became the haunt of botanists. The gardens were also exceptionally beautiful, making Singleton, in the eyes of George Frederick Cliffe, 'one of the most perfect places in the kingdom on a moderate scale a triumph of art'.

At the rear of the house was an archery range, a croquet lawn and an artificial grotto. Other romantic touches were a replica of an American log cabin and a Swiss Cottage of the sort P. F. Robinson had recently designed for Regent's Park. For the gate-keepers and their families he built two cottage lodges beside the coach road from Swansea. Singleton's farm, which became the home farm for the Vivian household, had a dairy herd, vines and fruit trees. By 1840 the new Singleton was a substantial estate crowned by an elegant mansion. Yet the house itself, constructed quickly on inadequate foundations, was poorly built. Twentieth-century repairmen dismiss it as jerry-built. Had Singleton been an ordinary house, built for shelter, the censure would be damning. But for the Vivians, as for most of the coppermasters, a house was a symbol: Singleton was meant to reflect the success of the Vivians, and it did this effectively for more than a century.

In the end Prichard took no action, but his note was a portent of what lay ahead of the coppermasters.

The Mansell Phillips Indictment

In 1820 the smoke issue surfaced again when Mansell Phillips, High Sheriff of Glamorgan and a landowner in the lower Tawe Valley, indicted the Vivians for common nuisance. Phillips first preferred the bill at Swansea but the Grand Jury, who saw it as a threat to the prosperity of the town, promptly rejected it. Phillips then re-preferred the bill at Cardiff, where it was upheld, and had he not relented the case would have gone to trial.[3] On learning that the Vivians were determined to suppress the smoke rather than, as an attending lawyer put it, 'be intimidated into purchasing security from the proceeding', Phillips withdrew the bill.[4]

In spite of the reprieve, for the Vivians and their fellow coppermasters the writing was clearly on the wall. Reports persisted of damage to fields and crops and a letter in May 1822 issues of the *St James Chronicle* and the *Cambrian* pointed to smoke damage to animals as well as crops, the author alleging that the teeth of horses were layered with copper. For Arthur Jones, John Henry Vivian's father-in-law who supervised work in the gardens of Marino, the letter was the 'composition of a madman' who might just as well have suggested that ships in Swansea harbour be laid keel up to save the expense of coppering.[5] But the reports of smoke damage were too persistent to be dismissed and, in any case, they were not contested by the Vivians. The implications of a growing climate of complaint and litigation sent ripples of anxiety through the town. Anxious to protect its golden goose from the attacks of aggrieved landowners, the portreeve had, in May 1820, called for a public meeting to consider measures, 'consistent with the prosperity of the works', that might be taken to abate the smoke.[6]

For several weeks, too, the Mansell Phillips indictment dominated the thrice-weekly correspondence between John Vivian in Cornwall and his son John Henry in Swansea. The elder Vivian remarked that demands for damages, where the plaintiffs asked only for money, were serious enough but 'indictments [that could enforce the closure and removal of the works] were the very d---l'.[7] He feared that if indicted John Henry would have to return to the house in Truro where the Vivians would all become 'Gentlemen . . . instead of copper smelters'. To escape that debilitating fate, they were prepared to move their works to Pembrey, on the Burry estuary, where there were fewer people and less cultivated land.[8]

In the Vivian letters there is no hint of vindictiveness toward Mansell Phillips. Both father and son conceded that a landowner forced to reduce rents by smoke-damage from their works had 'ample cause for complaint' and ought to receive an annual payment for damages.[9] John Vivian suggested that a barrister might be able to assess the 'quantum' of damage sustained, provided – and here he must have sensed a possible line of defence – he was satisfied that 'all the deterioration [had] been caused by our works'. But both Vivians also realized that to yield in this one case would be to trigger an avalanche of grievances not only against themselves but against the copper industry as a whole. As owners of the Hafod works they were the most obvious target for disgruntled landowners, but in theory any copper smelter could be indicted, or sued for damages. For the protection of the industry, two approaches seemed possible: they and their fellow smelters could either seek legislation against gratuitous or malevolent actions, or they could look for ways to suppress the smoke.[10]

For John Henry Vivian the decision was an easy one. He was, for the period, a rare example of an industrialist who was also deeply interested in science. In 1820, experimental science was just beginning to lengthen its stride, and it must have seemed inconceivable to him that it would not solve the smoke problem. Unlike most of his contemporaries and fellow industrialists, Vivian had the benefit of a scientific and technical education. While his elder brother, Richard Hussey Vivian, had taken the high road to Harrow and Oxford, and followed these with a brilliant career in the Army, John Henry attended the local grammar school at Lostwithiel. From Lostwithiel, at the age of sixteen, he went to Marburg in Germany to study commerce and languages, and from there to the Mining Institute of the University of Freiburg, in the Black Forest. In Germany a technical and scientific education carried no stigma. At Freiburg Vivian's subjects were metallurgy, chemistry, mathematics and mineralogy, the latter taught by the celebrated geologist Abraham Werner with whom Vivian was to correspond until Werner's death. While at Freiburg Vivian also toured the mining regions of Germany, Austria and Hungary, and visited most of the major smelting works in Europe. It was an education, combining the theoretical and the practical, for which Britain then could offer no parallel.[11]

A Fund to Obviate the Inconvenience Arising from Copper Smoke

On his return to Britain, John Henry Vivian, now a trained metallurgist, moved naturally into the south Wales end of his father's business and within a few years of his arrival, in 1806, he was experimenting with within six months of the opening of the competition, nuisances associated with five constituents of the smoke: arsenious vapours, fluoric, sulphuric, and sulphurous acids, and mechanical impurities. Their main quarry, the copperman's 'great enemy', as John Henry Vivian had once characterized it, was sulphurous acid gas, a mere one twenty-eighth part of the whole.

Bevington Gibbins experimented at the Rose works in Swansea, Vivian at the Hafod works and William Weston Young on open ground near Neath. All three began by building long flues from the calcining furnaces to the stacks.[19] A long horizontal flue encouraged the smoke to release some of its solid particles, and it also gave the experimenters time to treat the smoke before it entered the atmosphere. Gibbins experimented with ignited charcoal and Weston Young with fire, their objectives being to attack the offending gases with hot coals in the one case, flames in the other.

Young's experiments were the most dramatic. With funds donated by an unnamed benefactor, he built at Cadoxton, near Neath, a calcining furnace, a long horizontal flue and a vertical stack. At intervals in the flue he cut openings so that he might test the strength of the smoke and at the end of it he lit a wood fire through which the smoke from about a ton of heated ore was made to pass. Friendly observers declared that such smoke as emerged from the stack could be seen only by the sharpest eyes and then only against a background of trees. Two men who sat on the top of the stack, while workmen below stirred the ore in the furnace, announced that even though they breathed deeply and repeatedly over the mouth of the stack they suffered none of the choking symptoms usually associated with inhaling copper smoke. Plants, too, were unaffected. One was dug from a garden nearby, potted, and then placed on the rim of the stack. Several hours later it was said to have been none the worse for wear.

Although the judges were to disagree, Weston Young declared that he had 'totally decomposed' the arsenic and sulphur in the smoke. Ever the opportunist, he also announced that he was ready to build flues of a similar type for interested smelters at a cost of not more than £120. On reflection, however, he decided that he could do even better than this. So great was his confidence in the design that he offered to build the flues at his own expense provided the coppermasters would hand over the deposits of copper that accumulated in them.[20]

In a private proposal to the copper companies, which seems to have been written before the competition, Weston Young offered two schemes: a wet scheme, using shower chambers in the stack, at a cost of £700 and a dry scheme, requiring a much longer flue, at a cost of £1,000. In both cases, however, he offered to absorb the costs of building provided he could recover the copper deposits. In an environmentally sensitive aside, rare for the period, he pointed out that one advantage of the dry method – which produced no effluent – was that it would spare the lives of fish in nearby rivers and streams.[21]

John Henry Vivian's experiments were of a different order. To solve the smoke problem he engaged three of the most 'knowing heads' (his father's phrase) in Britain: the physicist and chemist Michael Faraday; Faraday's mentor, Sir Humphry Davy; and Professor Richard Phillips, a distinguished chemist. Also in attendance, but as an informed observer rather than a participant, was William Hyde Wollaston, the eminent chemist and physicist.[22] Of the three participants, Faraday and Phillips were the principal investigators, Davy an active adviser. Davy was a fellow Cornishman while Phillips, a Londoner, had family connections in both Swansea and Cornwall. Phillips was chairman of the Chemical Society and editor of the *Annals of Philosophy*. When in Swansea both Faraday and Davy stayed at Singleton.[23] Davy was 'exceedingly fond' of shooting Vivian's woodcock and there is a suggestion that he might have timed his visits to coincide with the season. In a letter from London thanking Vivian for the gift of several brace of woodcock, Davy deeply regretted that he had not been present at their demise.[24] When hunting at Singleton, he wore a red hat band for safety.

As a trained scientist familiar with the principles of physics and chemistry and well versed in natural history, Vivian was by no means out of place in this company. He was an early member of the Geological Society and a keen collector of minerals. At Singleton cabinets of minerals, classified according to principles laid down by Abraham Werner, were prominently displayed. Zoology was another interest and to indulge it he filled an entire room with stuffed birds and animals. In 1835 he would be a founder member, and first vice-president, of the Swansea Philosophical and Literary Institution (later the Royal Institution of South Wales) and in 1846 he would help found the Cambrian Archaeological Association.

But Vivian's chief scholarly achievement came relatively early, while he was still in his thirties. On the strength of an essay on the processes of smelting copper, published in the *Annals of Philosophy* (1823), he was elected to a fellowship of the Royal Society. His sponsors were Sir Humphry Davy, a past president of the Society, and Michael Faraday. Vivian's association with Davy, Faraday and Phillips was, for the period, a rare attempt to marry industrial practice and scientific theory. Science had scarcely begun to impinge upon basic industries and the kind of precise control over industrial operations sought by Vivian was virtually unknown. Novel, too, was his effort to get scientific minds to address the problems of industrial waste and pollution.

with atmospheric gases and cool before reaching the ground. In flat, open areas he thought stacks of 150 or 200 feet would serve the purpose.

Vivian ended his report by reminding his audience that in their efforts to solve the smoke problem the owners of Hafod had spared neither effort nor expense. Direct expenses alone amounted to more than £6,000 and to these had to be added the costs of diverting water from the Forest rolling mills, the extra consumption of coal and other materials and losses in production through stoppages when altering the flues. Nor, he argued, could the motives of the Vivians be impugned. They had started experimenting well before Mansell Phillips's indictment and continued long after its rejection by a Swansea jury. And although they had failed to rid the smoke of all its harmful gases, they could at least claim to have 'abated [the nuisance] to a degree beyond the possibility of its producing ... future cause for complaint'.

Vivian also argued that the thoroughness of their efforts, and the importance of the copper industry to Swansea and Great Britain as a whole, established a case for granting Hafod and the other works legal protection from further indictments. Closing the works and moving to another location was no solution even supposing one could be found 'distant from the haunts of man' and convenient to a river for a supply of water. In a few years villages and towns would grow around the works and the more querulous inhabitants would begin to complain of nuisances that had been the source of prosperity in the first place. It was a dilemma from which there was no escape.

In a postscript, Vivian quoted from a letter written to him by Davies Gilbert, vice-president of the Royal Society. Gilbert had been nominated to the Swansea adjudication committee but ill health had prevented him from participating. In the letter he declared that he had read both Vivian's description of the experiments and the reports of Faraday and Phillips. Although the experiments confirmed his belief that the methods of science – a 'correct theory of chemistry ... supported by minute experiments' – had no place in the rough and ready world of industry, he acknowledged the value of such plain and simple expedients as long flues, tall stacks and water treatments, and hoped that they would serve both as models for fellow smelters and as a brake on public expectations. An enterprise that enriched the entire community would, he hoped, be allowed the latitude of a little unavoidable nuisance.

The committee of judges delivered its report in December 1822 to a general meeting of Subscribers to the Fund for Obviating the Smoke chaired by William Grove, an eminent physicist and then portreeve of Swansea. The judges first commended Bevington Gibbins for his perseverance and skill but regretted that the impracticability of his methods debarred him from the prize. While conceding that Gibbins had 'practically succeeded' in decomposing the sulphurous acid in the smoke, the committee endorsed Vivian's view that as well as seriously reducing the draught in the furnaces the method used inordinate amounts of charcoal.

Weston Young, in the view of the committee, had least claim on the prize, in spite of a flattering report on his experiments in the *Monthly Magazine* and the aggressive claims of Young himself. Young complained of inadequate and infrequent inspection of his experiments but the judges insisted they had seen enough to conclude that even if the flames at the end of the flue had eliminated all the noxious gases in the smoke they did so only at the expense of the draught in the furnaces.[26]

Although more critical of Vivian's efforts than Davies Gilbert, the active members of the adjudicating committee reserved their highest praise for the experiments at Hafod. They expressed admiration for Vivian's 'indefatigable industry' and conceded that he had achieved 'a very decided abatement' of the nuisance by eliminating the arsenious vapours, the fluoric, the sulphuric, and sulphurous acids, and some trifling mechanical deposits. But the great enemy itself – the sulphurous acid gas – was still at large and Vivian, too, was denied the prize. The 'knowing heads' had failed.

At Hafod, the high stack and flues were kept in operation until the middle of 1832, with, in Vivian's estimate, the 'best results'. These might not have been good enough to win the prize but they were impressive enough to convince the inhabitants of Aberafan to insist, in the lease for a copper works site on Aberafan burrows, that the prospective owners build flues and stacks along Vivian lines.[27] Vivian himself had such confidence in his method that in 1832 he decided to extend the system of long flues, shower chambers and high stacks to all the furnaces at Hafod. For this he needed two new stacks, one at each end of the works, and a new network of flues with a combined length of half a mile. Into the smaller stack, 120 feet high, led flues from the roasting and melting furnaces. A shower chamber at the base of the stack absorbed the soluble gases and washed out the solid particles in the smoke.

For the much more toxic smoke from the calcining furnaces the Vivians built a stack so high that in clear weather it was a landmark for ships approaching Swansea. Resting on a block of masonry embedded in a slag heap 60 feet high, it reached 244 feet above the floor of the works. Through the stack, and the two shower chambers at its base, passed the smoke from all the calciners in Hafod. The new stacks and flues represented an outlay of an additional £5,000 at a time when trade in copper was far from brisk. John Henry Vivian was convinced that he had reduced the solid impurities and noxious gases to the minimum quantity compatible with practical smelting. This being the case, all that he and his associates could hope for, in the absence of protective legislation, was that the good sense and good feeling of their countrymen would keep them from harassing the company with prolonged and vexatious indictments. Not only did the new stack, in Vivian's eyes, entirely change the appearance of the smoke, but such smoke as there was had never been seen to touch the ground: 'It clears the neighbouring hills and becomes dispersed and diluted in the atmosphere as to become innoxious.'[28]

A Cornish mine 'captain' (Thomas Daniell) initiating a mining adventurer (Captain Morcom) in the art of assessing and mining copper ore. In the background is the engine house of a copper mine (Oil painting by John Opie, 1786). *Royal Institution of Cornwall.*

A view of Neath and the lower Nedd valley, looking north from the riverside. On the far right above the town is the Mackworth estate and Gnoll house. The copper works were downriver and west and south of the town (Painting by Thomas Hornor, 1816). *National Museums and Galleries of Wales.*

(Above) Copper ore barques 'taking the ground' in Swansea harbour (Photograph by Richard Calvert Jones, 1847.) Calvert Jones, a renowned photographer of ships and shipping, preferred his subjects lying high and dry. *National Maritime Museum London.*

(Left) William Richards (1819–1914), merchant and shipbuilder, of Swansea and New Bideford. *Prince Edward Island Public Archives and Records Office.*

Morris Lane, Swansea in 1852 (William Butler). The lane led from the High Street to the Strand and the recently built North dock. *City and County of Swansea Museum Service.*

Barque under construction at William Richards's New Bideford shipyard, Prince Edward Island. The Island's shelving beaches were ideal for shipbuilding and lumber was available both on the Island and in the neighbouring province of New Brunswick. *P. E. I. Museum and Heritage Foundation Collection, Prince Edward Island Public Archives and Records Office.*

'Morris Castle', *c.* 1880. *City and County of Swansea Museum Service.*

Workers' cottages, Morriston. Moulded slag coping stones, as on the wall in the left foreground, were a familiar sight in the copper-smelting districts. *Reproduced from originals held by the West Glamorgan Archive Service.*

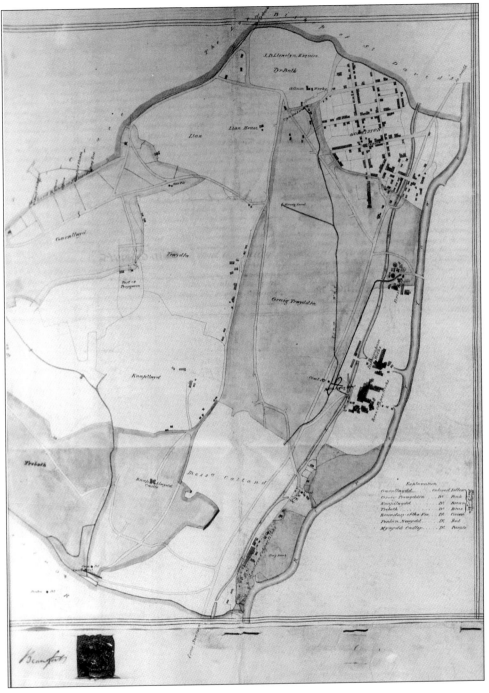

Map showing the planned town of Morriston, Craig Trewyddfa and the Beaufort coalholdings, and copper works along the Tawe, 1845. *Whiterock M17, The Archives of the Library and Information Services, University of Wales Swansea.*

The library and two-storey workers' housing at Cwmafan, built by the English Copper Company, *c*. 1847. By 1907, the date of the photograph, the lower floors of the buildings had been converted to shops. *Port Talbot Historical Society*.

Copperworkers beside the casting house at Taibach, *c*. 1884. *Port Talbot Historical Society*.

Three Swansea copperworkers, *c*. 1890s. *City and County of Swansea Museum Service*.

Clasemont, the Morriston home of the Morris family (T. Rothwell, 1792). In the foreground is William Edwards's famed, single-span Wychtree bridge. Edwards also devised the plan for John Morris's model town. *City and County of Swansea Museum Service.*

Singleton Abbey following the completion of P. F. Robinson's rebuilding in 1837. The engraving is after a drawing by Robinson himself. The mounted figures might have been John and Sarah Vivian. *The Archives of the Library and Information Services, University of Wales Swansea.*

John Collins and 'Moc' Morgan 'poling' copper at the Morfa works. *Reproduced from originals held by the West Glamorgan Archives Service.*

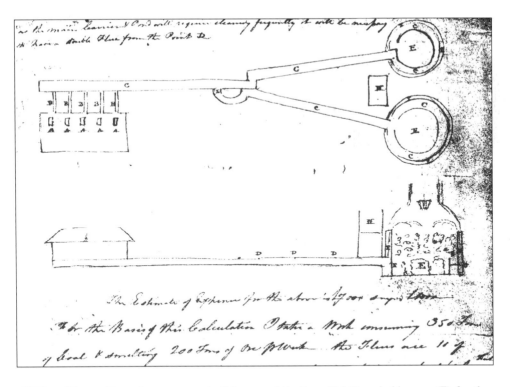

William Weston Young's arrangement of furnaces (A), flues (B&C) and chimneys (E) for the elimination of toxic gases from copper smoke, 1821–2. *Reproduced from originals held by the West Glamorgan Archive Service.*

Smoke from the Hafod and Middle Bank works about 1860. Between the two works is the river Tawe. *City and County of Swansea Museum Service.*

Rheola House, the home of Nash Edwards Vaughan (Painting by Thomas Hornor, 1815–16). Improved and extended by John Nash, the great Regency architect, Rheola was the architectural showpiece of the Nedd valley. *National Museums and Galleries of Wales.*

(Above) Lady Emily Charlotte Talbot (1840–1918). *Collection of John Vivian Hughes, Port Talbot.*

(Right) Chief Justice Sir John Campton ('Long') Lawrance who presided over the 1895 smoke trial at the Glamorgan Summer Assizes, Swansea. *Mansell Collection/ TIME INC.*

Cwmafan in the picturesque phase of the industrial revolution (G. Hawkins, Jr., 1839). Stac y Foel and the culvert connecting it to the copperworks below are on the right side of the painting. On the left is Coed Parc house and in the centre a round-arched tinplate works. *National Museums and Galleries of Wales.*

Ruins of the White Rock copperworks, before reclamation. Kilvey Hill is to the left, the river Tawe to the right. *National Monuments Record for Wales.*

5

The Great Copper Trials

John Henry Vivian's reasonable expectation that his efforts to suppress the smoke would moderate public demands, and mollify neighbouring farmers and landowners, proved vain. At the very time he was heightening stacks and extending flues at the Hafod works, farmers a few miles up the valley were organizing a legal campaign against him and his fellow coppermasters. By failing to absorb the sulphurous acid gas, long flues and shower chambers had produced no appreciable diminution in the toxicity of the smoke. Nor, too, had there been any noticeable reduction in the amount of smoke drifting up the valley. Ignoring Vivian's example, and the exhortations of Davies Gilbert, William Grove and the Committee to the Fund for Obviating the Smoke, neighbouring smelters had not lengthened their flues, heightened their stacks or installed shower chambers. Surrounding Hafod were hundreds of low stacks and chimneys, each one sending a spiral of smoke into the great white cloud that hung like a mantle over the Tawe. On clear days, when high-level temperature inversions capped the smoke and prevented it from dispersing, the cloud could be seen from distances of twenty and thirty miles.

Vivian's prediction, too, that smoke issuing from tall stacks would clear the sides of the valley and dissipate harmlessly in the upper atmosphere had been optimistic. He had failed to allow for the weight of sulphurous acid gas and the unusual configuration of the lower Tawe valley. Deep and narrow in the neighbourhood of the Hafod works, the valley trapped the smoke and, with the help of the prevailing westerlies, channelled it upstream. When the smoke eventually came to ground, a few miles above Hafod, local farmers claimed that it affected a larger area than it might otherwise have done because of its longer passage through the air.

Unmoved by the Vivians' appeal for restraint, a group of farmers from Llansamlet, a village in the Tawe valley about four miles above Swansea, demanded compensation for injuries to land, crops and stock from Hafod itself and from each of the other copper works downwind of the village. In a letter to the *Cambrian* their solicitor, William Meyrick, pointed out that the farmers expected only 'reasonable compensation' but in all cases their requests had been rejected, or simply ignored.[1] To retaliate, the farmers singled out those works they considered chiefly responsible for the damage and indicted their owners for public nuisance. Not only were copper works a source of intolerable smells and stenches but they injured people passing and repassing on commons, public highways, streets, lanes and passages.[2] In an effort to prevent litigation, which could only be costly and abrasive, Sir John Morris offered to mediate between the aggrieved farmers and the offending copper companies, but the offer was not taken up.[3] Bills of indictment presented to Grand Juries at Cardiff and Cowbridge were rejected, but in 1833 the farmers, represented by Thomas David of Llansamlet, succeeded in founding a bill at Carmarthen. The subjects of the indictment were John Henry Vivian and his brother Sir Richard Hussey Vivian, joint owners of the Hafod works and, ironically, the only smelters to have mounted a serious attack on the smoke. The action came before the Carmarthen Quarter Sessions, March 1833.

The Carmarthen Trial

For the Vivians the trial was pivotal. Although there was no danger that the works would have to close, as John Vivian had feared in 1820 at the time of the Mansell Phillips indictment, a loss would entail continual harassment from aggrieved farmers and a string of claims for damages. The Vivians and their counsel were convinced that the object of the indictment was not to close the works, or even abate the smoke, but to 'extort' money for damages.[4] A clear victory, on the other hand, would mean virtual immunity from prosecution. In a letter to John Henry Vivian, Richard Hussey Vivian – who was only nominally involved in the trial – had no doubt that his father and brother would 'fight the good fight' on behalf of the company but it was a contest the Vivians had no intention of losing.[5] To make certain of victory they engaged a heavy-weight: Sir James Scarlett KC, former Attorney General (in Wellington's administration), the future (and first) Baron Abinger and, by general acclaim, the leading counsel at the English Bar.

In 1833, Sir James Scarlett was at the height of his powers. After taking silk in 1816 he had enjoyed, according to his son Peter Scarlett, 'a longer series of success than has ever fallen to the lot of any other man in the law'.[6] Even allowing for filial bias, Sir James Scarlett was by far the most successful advocate of his day. Yet he was neither an outstanding lawyer nor a particularly articulate one. His strengths were Rumpolean ones. He is said to have had a thorough knowledge of human nature, perfect quickness of perception and decision, and – his most valuable asset – imperturbable self-possession. To these could be added certain non-Rumpolean qualities: good looks, a gentlemanly bearing and a finely modulated voice.

In court his manner was imperious. He was renowned for never taking notes of evidence and for a tendency to eschew cross-examination, relying, instead, on his powers of argument. Though an able speaker, he was never seen to prepare a speech; his gift, so it was said, was an ability to penetrate to the heart of things. Advocacy was in his blood. His chief defects are said to have been excessive vanity and a want of impartiality. When later elevated to the bench he proved to be a disastrous judge, seldom presenting more than one side of a case to the jury. His fee reflected his reputation: an unheard of (for Carmarthen) 400 guineas.

Sir James Scarlett's opponent was John Evans from Merthyr Tydfil, an able barrister but one with no reputation outside Glamorgan. So one-sided was the contest that John Evans sought immediately to turn the imbalance to his advantage. Although a Carmarthen jury would prove no more amenable to farming interests than a Glamorgan one, Evans cast himself and his client as underdogs. He acknowledged Sir James Scarlett's pre-eminence – 'the great Leader of the English Bar' – and pointed to the might and power of the Vivians. In 1833 John Henry Vivian was also the Liberal member for Swansea. His client, by contrast, was a humble tenant farmer – technically 'an inferior Yeoman or small Farmer' – and his advocate merely a local barrister. Only with God and the right on their side could they possibly hope for redress; in a battle of wits or a war of words, Evans conceded, he and Thomas David would stand no chance.[7]

To add to the imbalance, the Vivians were also supported by the entire populations of Swansea, Neath and Llanelli. Town was firmly and unevenly ranged against country. It was a classic confrontation in yet another sense. Swansea was the most English and, by definition in mid-nineteenth-century Wales, the most progressive of Welsh towns. Llansamlet, on the other hand, was in one of the few remaining Welsh-speaking parishes in the hundred of Swansea. In the eyes of progressives, the village also lay beyond an agricultural pale. On the fringes of upland Glamorgan, Blaenau Morgannwg, it had not been touched by the new agriculture developed in the English lowlands. It was a parish dominated by, as Swansea's most eminent physician (Dr Thomas Williams) would put it, 'rude and primitive agiculturists'.[8]

John Evans began his prosecution by describing the Welsh process of smelting and the growth in Hafod's smelting capacity. Since the opening of the works in 1811, the number of furnaces had virtually doubled. He described, too, the general effects of copper smelting on land and vegetation. Immediately above Swansea the Tawe valley was a wasteland of slag heaps, ruined soil and 'stag-headed' trees. Copper smoke, 'like a giant Upas tree', spread desolation all around. Grasses and heather had withered and died, and hedgerows and trees, except for a few skeletal trunks, had disappeared. Topsoil, no longer secured by plant roots and fibre, had been washed from the slopes, and the exposed subsoil eroded into a badland of ridges and gulleys. Corn and haylands failed, and farms had to be abandoned. There were four derelict farms in the neighbour-hood of the Hafod works alone. Cattle that grazed on smoke-impregnated pastures sickened and died, and humans enveloped by smoke suffered a variety of ailments. To support the allegations, and provide what he hoped would be telling detail, John Evans drew on a long list of witnesses.

Morgan Morgan testified that the parish of St John had once been good corn, hay and pasture land – a place of 'capital' crops but now not 'corned' at all. All was now barren and what was left no cattle would eat. The once verdant Kilvey Hill, directly across the valley from Hafod, was 'as barren as a road'. In the parish many farms were untenanted, yet all had once been occupied. He remembered oak, ash and sycamore, but they had all died within the previous twenty years: 'they die standing, and are cut down afterwards'. Though loss of amenity was not an issue at the trial, laments for a landscape that had once been attractive was a persis-tent refrain in the testimony. The witnesses sang, as one commentator would later remark, of times not before the flood, but before the smoke.[9] Names alone were evocative: Glandwr, water's edge; Hafod, summer dwelling; Cae Morfa Carw, marshland where the deer grazed.

Morgan Morgan also pointed out that copper smoke drifting across the King's highway – the main Neath–Swansea road – was a hazard to humans and animals. Technically, therefore, it was a public nuisance. The smoke could stop the breath of horses, if they were being driven fast, and also discomfit passengers. The acrid taste of the smoke lodged in the mouth and nostrils and had to be washed out on arrival in Swansea. The smoke also made the breath short and the eyes smart. As an antidote to the irritants in the smoke, Morgan Morgan had begun taking snuff, first from paper, then, as the need grew more insistent, from a box.

In his cross-examination Sir James ignored the details of the testimony. His main objective was to attach mocking labels to the lead witness and the Llansamlet farmers. Morgan Morgan he addressed as 'the Counsellor' because of his interest in law and his role as intermediary between the farmers and William Meyrick, their solicitor. Sir James elicited from Morgan the information that he had given evidence at all the attempts to found bills of indictment (eight at Cowbridge and two at Cardiff) against the copper companies. The farmers he labelled 'the Club', pointing out that the costs of the prosecution had been met by a subscription fund. Though belittling, the designation was kinder than the one applied later by Dr Thomas Williams of Swansea. For Williams the Llansamlet farmers were a 'joint stock, hostile company' whose only purpose was to ply the proprietors of the copper works with 'vexatious proceedings at law'.[10]

Witnesses who followed Morgan Morgan gave details of damage to land, crops and stock. Thomas Hopkins, who had kept stock until the completion of the Hafod works, testified that cattle subjected to copper smoke became lame and either refused to feed or were unable to do so. In some cases the smoke made their teeth grow one over the other so the animals were unable to chew. On opening, or dissecting, the cattle he also found that their lungs had worn away. In the smoke districts the ailments were so consistent that they were given a name: *efryddod*, or crippling disease.

William Hitchman, the second witness, had left Cadoxton for Llansamlet ten years previously, bringing his cattle with him. After ten or eleven months they began to get lame. Some sank to their knees, others fell on their hindquarters and their ribs broke in pieces. Horses also wasted away, unable to feed because their teeth blackened and decayed. Large lumps also appeared on their knees and joints. Fruit trees taken to Llansamlet fared no better than stock; they were 'blasted' by the smoke and did not bear. In six years he had made nothing from the farm even though he was brought up a farmer.

Richard Bowen farmed about two miles from Hafod. After the building of the works his cattle became lame, their hooves 'grew wild' and their ribs broke. Lumps as big as fists grew on their legs. Some of the cattle fed lying down, others on their knees; they could not stand up to feed and they had no milk. Zechariah Jenkins had farmed near Hafod for seven years. His cattle failed to graze, their front teeth loosened and eventually fell out. In the preceding three years he had lost five cows, four calves and a mare. There were great lumps on their legs and when he opened the beasts he found that their lungs were rotten. He had also lost much hay and corn. Crops were particularly vulnerable when in blossom and during wet weather when water acted as a solvent for the poisons in the smoke. Fields of corn could be ruined in a matter of hours. When recalled to the witness stand later in the day he produced the swollen leg of a cow that had been killed by *efryddod*.

Jane Wilks, a widow, had farmed in Llansamlet for forty-eight years and until the smoke came she had prospered. Her testimony was an inadvertent offering to the defence. She volunteered that when the wind was from the west, Hafod and Middle Bank smoke mingled: 'It all came together like a river.' She had asked the proprietors of both works to buy her land, but both had refused. Vivian had contended that his smoke was no more harmful than the smoke of his competitors, and when she approached him during her late husband's illness he gave her £5 because of her low estate and the failure of her crops.

William Evans listed the ailments of a horse that had been young and healthy when brought to Llansamlet. Eleven years later its legs were all lumps and there were even lumps on its jaw. It could scarcely walk. Evans had vegetable gardens at Llangyfelach – on the west side of the Tawe and unaffected by the smoke – and at Llansamlet. His Llangyfelach garden throve but the vegetables from his Llansamlet garden, though they did well at first, were no longer edible.

George Cudlip, one of two English witnesses for the prosecution, had been raised on a farm in Devon. His father, the master of a vessel trading West Country meal, flour and grain for Welsh culm and coal, had brought him to Swansea. When he began farming, in 1822, his crops were good. In 1826 smoke touched his corn, striking it just under the ear, and it produced very little. Since 1830 he had lost nine cows and seven horses, all to the smoke. Blue in colour, and with a disagreeable taste, the smoke could sicken animals within a week. The teeth of his cattle had worn and become black, knobs had grown on their legs, ribs had split in two and bones become honey-combed and rotten. His farm, of 60 acres, which he had leased from Lord Jersey for fourteen years, had reduced him to penury. He limed and manured it every year even though there was no longer any point in attempting to farm well in Llansamlet. When cross-examined he admitted that he could not distinguish Hafod smoke from White Rock or Middle Bank smoke.

William Hopkin farmed land that had also been worked by his father. He, too, limed and manured his land every year even though, like George Cudlip, he considered it a waste of time to do so. In 1832 his crops had been very light even though he mucked and limed his fields. The smoke, he testified, could ruin a crop in one night. When cross-examined he admitted that he was a member of the 'the Club', and that he hoped to recover some of his losses; he had not been at Cowbridge with 'Counsellor' Morgan.

William Harries, a native of Llanelli, had farmed for three years in the Llansamlet district. In the second year he lost three cows, and in the third three horses and a colt. The colt had a gathering under its jaw bone from which bone marrow ran out. From the outset his crops were poor; corn produced plenty of straw but no grain. After three years of successive losses he had given up the farm. Thomas David, chairman of the group and the plaintiff at the trial, worked three small farms, about 90 acres in all. Within a year of Vivian putting 'fire in his works' he had lost three fields of corn. He took samples of damaged corn to Vivian's house, but to no avail. Each year the smoke touched some part of his farms which were now so unproductive that not for ten years had it been worth his while to employ a man regularly. His losses in the past year amounted to £50 or £60, and had Vivian's solicitors offered him that much in compensation he would have been satisfied. When they refused he preferred the indictment.

David Sims had suffered his first losses eighteen or nineteen years earlier. After a few years he moved to a new farm a mile further off, but the smoke had found him out. He had been to Carmarthenshire and Pembrokeshire to get healthy cattle but they had all sickened; cattle bought in Narberth in November were lame by April. When the cows could no longer stand he cut the grass and lay it beside them. This, he declared, was common practice in Llansamlet. He had found that the thicker the skin of the cattle, the better able they seemed to withstand the smoke. When he opened the dead beasts there was scarcely any liver or lights to be found. He read many books in the hope of finding a cure for his cattle, but the remedies never matched the ailments. He was never able to cure one.

When cross-examined, Sims, too, was dubbed a 'Counsellor'. He had gathered evidence against the Vivians and urged farmers who had suffered losses to testify at the trial. But not to be intimidated, Sims retorted that he wished he were indeed a counsellor because it would be a far better trade than farming in Llansamlet. He admitted to being a member of 'the Club' and that he would have accepted £150 in damages, even though the amount was less than the losses actually sustained. Although his farm was closer by two miles to copper works in Neath Abbey than to Hafod, he would not concede that any of the damage came from the direction of Neath. Not one wind in fifty came from the east and his farm lay west of the Neath Abbey works.

There were only two non-farming witnesses for the prosecution. First, John Wood, Clerk of the Peace for the County of Glamorgan. For thirty-five years he had travelled regularly on the coach road between Neath and Swansea. When the smoke was 'down' and the wind from the south or south-west, it crossed the Tawe valley section of the road, and was sometimes so thick that the coachman had to alight and lead the horses with the aid of a lamp. In Mr Wood the smoke produced nothing more than a little nausea but his wife and children had, on one occasion, been violently sick.

The second non-farm witness was Perceval Johnson, a government metallurgist from Cornwall. He described how sulphur and atmospheric

As a contest the trial was over. For the prosecution there was no recovery from such a pummelling and the proceedings might well have ended at this point. All that remained for the defence was to seal the victory as tightly as possible. Sir James began the process by describing John Henry Vivian's prodigious efforts to suppress the smoke, and the heavy costs of building networks of flues and high stacks. Nothing within the power of science and capital to achieve had been spared in the effort to render the smoke innoxious. He claimed complete success for the experiments, even to the elimination of sulphurous acid gas. Exhalations from Hafod's highest stacks were, he asserted, 'totally incapable of producing any injurious effect whatever'.[12]

When speaking of injuries, however, Sir James was careful to restrict the discussion to the effects of copper smoke on humans. He noted that the prosecution had produced no old man afflicted with asthma, no delicate young woman with injured lungs and no apothecary and no physician to testify to its unwholesome effect on the human constitution. With the exception of Mr Wood's testimony there was not one atom of evidence to support the allegation that copper smoke endangered public health. Just as one swallow did not make a summer, one lady with an upset stomach – and this nine years before the trial – in no way proved that copper smoke was in any way harmful to the people of Swansea or the Tawe valley.

Instead of continuing to insist on the harmlessness of the smoke, Sir James Scarlett employed his imperturbable self-possession to reverse the equation. Far from being a danger to health, copper smoke was a blessing. During the preceding year, cholera had ravaged Glamorgan's coal and iron towns but had not touched a copper works community. The smoke was a prophylactic. It might irritate the eyes and sour the mouth but there was no questioning its overall beneficence. As evidence, he cited the healthful and florid countenances of the children in the copper works schools. Clearly, the charge that copper smoke endangered health was 'a complete fallacy'.

To round out its case, the defence then called witnesses. Eighty-three-year-old William Bevan, a former surveyor, land agent and accountant, contended that the face of the country had altered but very little in his lifetime. The inference was that any damage to the landscape had been done long before any of the plaintiffs began farming, and by the White Rock and Middle Bank rather than the Hafod works. He also observed that without the copper works Swansea would still be 'a mere fishing town'.

Bevan's fifty-eight-year-old son and namesake, an engineer who had worked in and around copper works for most of his life, testified that the appearance of Kilvey Hill had not changed during the past twenty-five years. He had once farmed and found that as long as he limed the land his corn and cattle never suffered, but when he substituted ashes for lime his cattle suffered a little. But starve the soil and expose cattle to damp, wet ground and westerly winds and they might have to be milked on their knees and raised from lying positions with ropes. A little shelter, lime and manure, he opined, would have saved the Llansamlet cattle. He knew of fields only 600 yards from the works, dressed liberally with lime, which some years earlier had produced a fine crop of hay. When cross-examined, however, he admitted that the farm (Pentremawr) lay on the west, upwind side of the works.

Henry Owen, a farmer and farm agent for Mansell Phillips, asserted that he had produced the best wheat on the Swansea market that year on a farm only half a mile from the Hafod works. As an agent for Phillips, who in 1820 had threatened to indict the Vivians for public nuisance, Owen was a telling witness. He explained how ten years earlier he and Phillips had found the farm, supposedly devastated by copper smoke, 'like a wilderness and without fences'. Undeterred, however, he had taken the farm in hand, pursued a proper course of husbandry and mended the fences. Penllwyn Robert was now a model farm. Copper smoke he regarded as nothing less than 'an admirable excuse for lazy farmers, bad husbandry and want of manure'. Before coming to Swansea Owen had farmed in Breconshire and had seen cattle diseases similar to *efryddod*, which he believed to have been caused by 'something in the fields'. When cross-examined by John Evans, Owen disclosed that his farm, too, lay west of the Hafod works.[13]

Owen's testimony was endorsed by the versatile and ubiquitous William Weston Young, in his role as land surveyor. He had been witness to the revival of Penllwyn Robert and considered it to be a 'show farm'. The teeth of its cattle were white and firm and the quality of its wheat as much above average, both in quality and quantity, as the prosecutor's was below. He was familiar with Thomas David's farm and ascribed its sorry condition to an unfortunate combination of cold, yellow soils and exceedingly bad husbandry. For good measure, he added that he had visited the Hafod works earlier that month and found the methods used to suppress the smoke to be completely effective.

Morgan Hussey, a copper refiner, declared that the horses used at the Hafod works were healthy and completely free of *efryddod*. John Evans, however, pointed out that the sulphurous and arsenious gases were carried away from the works and that the feed for the horses came from outside the district. Hussey also averred that he had never seen grass on Kilvey Hill, the side facing the works having always been rocky and barren. William Jones, the smelting agent for Hafod, affirmed that in general the workmen were as healthy as the horses and that as a work-force they were not susceptible to epidemic fevers. Jones had lived within the walls of the works for thirteen years and except for rheumatic attacks he had enjoyed excellent health.

The defence kept its most telling witnesses until the end of the trial. The destruction of a dozen farms in a relatively poor parish could be made light of, but the health of an entire community was another matter. Although the prosecution had been unable to produce witnesses to testify that smoke from the stacks endangered health, the question of health hung over every discussion about copper smoke. To dispel any doubts on the subject, the defence produced two Swansea physicians, Dr George Gwynne Bird and Dr Edward Howell, who testified that they knew of no ailment that could be attributed to copper smoke. On the contrary, people in the copper communities were healthy and lived as long as people elsewhere. Except for cholera, epidemics were uncommon, and even cholera was not as devastating as in other places. Dr Howell, who had practised for twenty years in Swansea, not only considered copper smoke harmless to humans, but declared it to be a proven antiseptic against ague and typhus.

It was close to midnight when the judge, Mr Justice Patteson, began his summing up. To save time, and perhaps allay any anxieties in the copper fraternity that the trial itself might not have dispelled, the foreman interrupted the judge to announce that no summation was necessary, the jurors having made up their minds. Judge Patteson pointed out that before a verdict could be rendered he was duty-bound to explain the law of public nuisance. He advised the jurors to disregard the defence's argument that Swansea would be ruined by an indictment of the Hafod works. A crime proved, he asserted, is a crime indictable, but to bring down a verdict of guilty the jurors had to be convinced that the nuisance was general, rather than particular, and that the alleged injuries had been caused by smoke from the Hafod works.

No sooner had Judge Patteson finished speaking than the foreman rose again to pronounce a verdict of not guilty. Two of the jurors, however, demurred, protesting that they had not been consulted and by their behaviour intimating that they disagreed with the verdict. Judge Patteson, who was about to leave the bench, resumed his seat while the jurors retired briefly to the Council Room. On their return, the two recalcitrant members having been brought into line, the foreman confirmed the initial verdict. When the news reached Swansea the following morning the town took to the streets. The *Cambrian* announced its 'heartfelt satisfaction' with a verdict that went to the 'very existence of the Copper trade of Swansea', and both Church and State rejoiced – the one by ringing bells throughout the day, and the other by firing cannon.[14]

The Brecon Trial

At the end of the Carmarthen trial Thomas David and the Llansamlet farmers may have been down, but they were far from out. In little more than a year they were back on their feet jousting with opponents only fractionally lighter than the Vivians. The motives for their Quixotic behaviour were never disclosed. At the second trial their counsel referred to a backer, 'known no less for his private worth than his high professional character', whose support had been critical in bringing the action. The compelling motive for the farmers' persistence, however, must have been their burning sense of injustice and a determination to get some redress for injuries to crops and stock. Their target for this second assault on the copper interests were the Grenfells, owners and operators of the Middle Bank works. The action was for damages, set at £3,000, and the venue the Breconshire Assizes, August 1834.

In the few years before the trial, David had preferred no fewer than eight bills of indictment against the Grenfells in an effort, as the Grenfells' legal advisers remarked, to extort money from the Company. The farmers' strategy, they elaborated, had been to prefer indictments in the far corners of the county against as many copper works as possible, in the mean time applying to the proprietors for damages. When the indictments failed they moved outside the county altogether. Rather than tolerate continued harassment, several companies had entered upon 'vague and uncertain arrangements' with the farmers. But this the Grenfells, resisting the temptation of a temporary quiet, had adamantly refused to do. And to save the industry as a whole from the importunate demands of every cottage owner within reach of the smoke, they had decided to let the matter come before a jury.[15] In spite of the single-mindedness of David's attack, the choice of Middle Bank as the target for indictment was to some extent arbitrary. English law demanded that in order to receive damages, the plaintiff had to isolate the offender. Middle Bank, just over a mile from one of David's three farms, seemed a logical choice. All three of the farms lay immediately downwind of the works.

Although the defendants and some of the legal counsel had changed, the trial itself was a replay of the trial at Carmarthen, if in a lower register.[16] Many of the same witnesses presented the same, or very similar, evidence. Those for Thomas David testified to the injuries inflicted by copper smoke on land, crops and stock, and to substantiate their claims they brought to Brecon a horse and a cow showing the symptoms of *ef-ryddod*. Counsel for the Grenfells, on the other hand, questioned the competence of Llansamlet farmers to husband land, grow crops and tend stock, even in circumstances more favourable than those found on the margins of the Welsh upland.

To justify singling out the Middle Bank works, David's counsel called Perceval Johnson, the government metallurgist who had testified at the Carmarthen trial. Johnson pointed out that under calcination the Anglesey ores used at Middle Bank produced roughly twice as much sulphurous acid gas as the Cornish ores used at Hafod. Adam Murray, a brash Scottish witness for the plaintiffs, introduced himself as the product of a country where there is a great deal of brains. His own testimony, however, demonstrated the contrary. He asserted that the tall stack at the Hafod works should have been very much higher, and that the chemical operations associated with it were 'all humbug'. Murray was a land agent for Lord Jersey, the owner of more than 3,000 acres in the parish of Llansamlet.

With the example of the Carmarthen trial to draw upon, the task of defending the Grenfells was a relatively simple one. Their counsel was quick to point out that the removal of the trial to Brecon was in itself an admission that no Glamorgan or Carmarthen jury would reduce to poverty and pauperism an entire region to satisfy the greed of a few farmers: ten individuals, as his brief had directed, 'hardly removed a grade above the peasantry'.[17] He also made the point that Middle Bank had a prescriptive right to smelt copper in the Tawe valley; the works had been 'smoking and flaming' fully twenty years before Thomas David had begun farming in Llansamlet. The plaintiff, therefore, had come to his lands with full knowledge of the impact of the works upon the countryside. But his most telling point was that at Carmarthen the plaintiff had sworn that the Hafod works had done him 'all of the injury'. Now, a mere sixteen months later, the finger of blame had shifted. If David was successful in the current action, where, he wondered, would it point to next, and what was to prevent him from picking off, one by one, all the other copper works on the Tawe? Defeat, of course, would end the harassment.

In his directions to the jury at the close of the fourteen-hour trial, the judge, Baron J. Parke, advised the members to cast from their minds the great benefits conferred by the Middle Bank works, and to address two questions: whether Thomas David had sustained damages from the Grenfell operations, and – if he had – whether any of the damage could be attributed to the growth of the works during the past twenty years. The jury retired for three-quarters of an hour before delivering its verdict. There was little comfort in it for Thomas David and the Llansamlet farmers. The jurors conceded that David had suffered losses, and that some of these losses were due in part to increases in the size of Middle

Bank and other works in the neighbourhood. The remaining losses, however, they attributed to poor husbandry. When asked by Baron Parke if they had calculated the amount of damage caused by Middle Bank smoke, their foreman answered that it was 'a thing impossible' to determine with the evidence before them. Lack of evidence, however, did not prevent him from affirming that whatever the amount it was less than the damage caused by the plaintiff's poor management of his lands. For Thomas David there was no way out, and to resolve the impasse his counsel intimated that he would settle for damages of 1 shilling.

For all the jury's protestations of incompetence to apportion blame, or to assess damages, the verdict was a diplomatic one. It demanded nothing from the Grenfells, either in terms of compensation to David or of adjustments in the operation of the Middle Bank works, and by attributing even a fraction of the injury to copper smoke it left Thomas David and the Llansamlet farmers with the vestiges of a moral victory.

class (apoplexy, palsy, etc.), and of the digestive organs, were equally uncommon.[4]

Observations such as these were balm not only to the coppermasters but to the merchants, hoteliers and professional men of the town. Swansea was an Elysium of good health. But neither the blessings of local physicians nor the blandishments of writers of town guides and directories were proof against official, objective scrutiny. The cholera epidemic of 1831–2 exposed the inadequacy both of existing sanitary facilities and the capacities of local commissions and trustees to manage them. Public health in British towns and cities could no longer be left entirely in local and, in some cases, private hands. The determination to impose national, uniform standards of sanitation upon a framework of local government in England and Wales culminated in the Public Health Act of 1848.[5] The Act called for a central board of health in London and local boards in the provinces. Once established, local boards in theory were required to exercise many of the functions specified in the Act. But in practice the local boards, except in cases of epidemic disease, were free to do as they chose. Many, for fear of raising the rates or, as in the case of Swansea, offending local industries, did very little.

The need for reform was also suggested by the statistics on disease and mortality then being compiled by insurance companies and the Statistical Department of the Board of Trade. Statistics were the rage of the 1830s. Even Swansea, which felt no need for sanitary reform, was affected. In 1836 the Philosophical and Literary Institution appointed a statistical committee to conduct studies of trade, population and health in Swansea and its neighbourhood. Though hungry for statistics, the committee seems to have had no great appetite for the truth. In its report the committee acknowledged that typhus had occurred among the poorer classes, and conceded that this might have had some connection with imperfect sewerage and filthy streets, but it still managed to conclude that generally speaking, compared with other places, 'epidemic diseases [in Swansea] are of an innocuous character'.[6] The committee's findings were reinforced in 1839 by J. M. G. Gutch, works surgeon to the Vivians, founder member and secretary of the Royal Institution and keen student of meteorology. In a paper to a medical journal he concluded that, as an agent in inducing disease, copper smoke was much less culpable than '*a priori* reasoning' might suppose. As proof he cited the great age of two women 'living in the midst of it'.[7]

The myth of Swansea as a citadel of health crumbled before the report of the Royal Commission appointed in 1843 to investigate the health of fifty of the largest towns in England and Wales. The report on Swansea, written by Sir Henry de la Beche, the distinguished geologist, was the first objective assessment of the health of the town. It revealed, of course, that Swansea was no healthier than other towns and somewhat less healthy than the countryside: mortality rates in Swansea were 23 per thousand compared with 15 per thousand in Gower. The rate for Swansea was lower than in some of the other towns but this, as Sir Henry explained, was a result of the masking of the high rate of infant mortality by the large number of adults who came to the town in search of work. Both typhus and consumption were widespread and the incidence of the latter was even higher in the copper districts than elsewhere. In Morriston, which was 'more frequently involved in copper smoke than Swansea', one in every three or four deaths was from consumption.[8]

For apologists for the smoke there was even worse to come: 'For deaths by epidemics generally, and including typhus, the rate of mortality at Swansea is high, closely followed by Cardiff; so that the supposed corrective influence of the copper-smoke for these diseases is not apparent.' Sir Henry conceded, out of deference to Swansea's physicians, that their claims for the benign influence of copper smoke on health 'could scarcely be doubted', but he immediately withdrew the concession by observing that such a conclusion 'is not very clearly seen from known data'. A sentence or two later he struck even more directly: 'The Llangafelach [sic] and town districts show a higher rate of mortality, and are those in which this should be expected from the occupations of the inhabitants, and the impurities from various causes, mingled with the air breathed.' How could one expect, he noted elsewhere in the report, that smoke virulent enough to scour window glass, and change within a few hours the colour of convolvulus, would not damage human tissue?[9]

In spite of the severity of Sir Henry's report Swansea's property owners, fearing an increase in the rates and offended by what they perceived as 'precipitous haste' in the conduct of the General Board of Health, objected to the implementation of the Health of Towns Act, 1848.[10] Ignoring their objection, the Board dispatched one of its superintending inspectors, the Merthyr engineer and historian George T. Clark, to report in detail on sanitary conditions in the town.[11] Clark was no more encouraging than Sir Henry de la Beche and, on the strength of his report and a recommendation by a town committee, the General Board of Health issued a provisional order vesting responsibility for the execution of the Public Health Act in the Swansea town council, acting as the local board of health.[12] On the question of copper smoke Clark was no more encouraging than Sir Henry, quoting in full Sir Henry's remarks on the ineffectualness of the smoke as an antiseptic or prophylactic. The *Cambrian* ignored this and all other censures, lighting on the report's one positive observation – the naming and lettering of the streets and courts 'dew-less, wood-less, [and] grass-less, this smoky desert is therefore poison-less'. Any standing bodies of water were so acidic that no plants or animals could live in them. Though hideous to the eye, this lifeless landscape was, in effect, life-giving; its passive, harmless mountains of siliceous and metallic ashes 'did good by negation'.

To drive home the point, Thomas Williams invited the reader to reverse the coin and paint the contrary scene:

> Clothe Kilvey Hill with a rich umbrageous forest: convert the treeless, shrubless waste of Llansamlet into a damp foliaceous jungle; let the evergreen wave over the stony declivities beneath the Castle of Morriston; restore the valley to its primeval morass, and how changed will be the climate! The expanse of leafy surface would augment the annual rainfall . . . The low places along the river banks would be changed into exhalent pools of rank vegetation. The stagnant waters would become slimy, and fevers would decimate a hapless population.

Thus in Sketty and places west, still dangerously vegetated, 'the fairest and most lovely [were] swept from a fond existence . . . the hale and rugged gardener, or the stout, merry milkmaid'.[25]

Had milkmaids and gardeners been fortunate enough to live within range of the copper smoke, its prophylactic qualities might well have saved them. Not only did the smelting districts produce no miasma but the smoke destroyed any that might have invaded from elsewhere:

> Does [the smoke] not, if anything, purify the air? . . . Has it not banished ague from the country? Is not the sphere of its distribution a demarcation defensive against the invasion of cholera? Is it not a most uncommon event to meet with a true case of typhus fever among the inhabitants of the smoke district? . . . Is not a cloud of copper-smoke a coat of mail against epidemic influenza, by decomposing the ozone of the air?

Typhus, according to Thomas Williams, had never been known in any of the villages immediately surrounding the copper works, and during the cholera epidemics of 1832, 1849 and 1854 the villages of Foxhole, Bonymaen, Landore and Viviantown, all engulfed in copper smoke, were marked by 'almost a perfect exemption'.[26]

Although most defenders of copper smoke readily conceded that it was no friend to vegetation, Thomas Williams was able to find saving graces. Wild vegetation, he observed, might wither at its touch but cultivated annuals such as the cabbage, the potato, the fuchsia and the dahlia flourished in gardens in the smoke districts. Potatoes, according to Thomas Williams, did particularly well. Not only had they an affinity for smoke but, within its protective shield, they suffered far less than other potatoes in the region from the blight that had laid waste the Irish crops. 'Smoke-potatoes', he declared, fetched the highest prices in the Swansea market.

For Thomas Williams copper smoke could do almost no wrong and his chief complaint was that there was too little of it. If only it were possible to maintain

> a permanent infusion of copper smoke within a given locality, the Author records his deliberate belief that the population of such a locality would be permanently exempt from all those epidemic diseases, whose causative germs, whatever they be in essence, travel and multiply, from place to place in the atmosphere.

The benefits extended even to depression. Low spirits and nervous depression, the products of a heavy, humid, maritime climate, were, he asserted, lifted by the dry air and soil of the adjacent smoke region.[27]

Copper smoke would never have a more remarkable champion than Thomas Williams, but he and his Swansea colleagues were by no means alone in the belief that copper smoke and copper itself were shields against infection. In October 1865, the *Cambrian* reported that a French physician – Dr V. Burg of Paris – believed copper with respect to cholera to be what quinine is with respect to malaria: 'a sovereign remedy'. He claimed that in 1832, 1849 and 1854, when cholera raced through France, copper workers always escaped infection, even when family, friends and neighbours were stricken. To protect his own patients, he dosed them with salts of copper and encouraged them to wear copper rings or plates.[28] Dissolved salts of copper had long been held to have curative properties. In an address to the Royal Society in 1760, Dr John Rutty characterized the 'vitriolic fluid' flowing from the copper workings in Parys Mountain, Anglesey, as 'a powerful detergent' capable of curing 'inveterate ulcers, the itch, scab, tetterous eruptions, dysenteries, internal haemorrages ... diorhea [sic]... the worms, agues, dropsies and jaundice'.[29]

Anti-Smoke Legislation

Though spirited, Thomas Williams's defence of copper smoke was a rearguard action – the rationalizations of an able but, as his tutor Richard Bright characterized it, 'impetuous' mind. Few disinterested observers shared his enthusiasm for copper smoke. The public health movement was gathering momentum, and foul air, like contaminated water and filthy streets, had become a target for official action. But of all pollutants, annual wage bill of £7,000. The company produced two-thirds of the United Kingdom's exports of patent fuel. Smelting houses might have been exempt from the 1847 law but, Grove reminded the jury, copper smoke had done far more damage to Swansea than patent fuel smoke. The time had long past, Grove noted darkly, when Swansea's prosperity could rest on its fame as a bathing and fishing town.

In his summing up the judge, Justice Thomas Falconer, emptied the question of the larger issues implicit in Grove's argument, and which must have occupied every mind in the courtroom. He warned the jurors against the danger of arrogating to themselves subjects that were outside their competence. They were not called upon to decide on questions concerning the prosperity of the town, nor was it within their province to alter the law of nuisance. The case in his view was a very simple one and had it not been for the introduction of 'irrelevant subjects' it would have attained no importance at all. The question before the jurors was this: had the plaintiffs' property suffered damage, and if so, how much? The case, as the historian Gerald Fiedler pointed out, had been reduced to the most innocuous level, ensuring that any legal precedents created by the verdict would have the smallest repercussions.[34] Even so, the jury agonized for six hours before awarding the plaintiffs damages of 40 shillings.

Three years later there was another equally ineffectual assault on smoke. In response to the 1855 Nuisances Removal and Diseases Prevention Act, people living downwind of a small wood naphtha plant at Blackpill, a few miles west of Swansea, complained formally of damage to trees and gardens and of giddiness and feelings of intoxication caused by fume from the plant. In the event of a complaint the Act empowered district highways boards to take the matter to a justice. But a formal complaint, backed by a petition from the affected property owners and a declaration from two physicians (Thomas Williams and W. Rowland) that the smoke was both a 'nuisance and injurious to public health', failed to move the Swansea Highways Board. As a wood rather than a mineral or coal-burning works, the naphtha plant, in the opinion of the Board, was not subject to the provisions of the Act.[35] A letter from one exasperated property owner, J. D. Berrington, to the General Board of Health prompted an exchange of letters between the General Board and the Swansea Highways Board but, the former having no real powers of coercion, it produced no further action.[36] The Highways Board postponed one monthly meeting and the following month tabled the issue until each member of the Board had been supplied with a copy of the Act. But familiarity with the Act did not, of course, affect the outcome. All the Board members, with the exception of the embarrassed chairman, declined to prosecute the matter of the 'alleged' Blackpill nuisance.[37]

Winds of Change

By mid-century the defenders of industrial smoke, buoyed by the Patent Fuel verdict and the success of an obdurate and evasive Highways Board, were so confident of their position that the bold few who continued to complain were told that in Swansea smoke now enjoyed a prescriptive right, sanctioned by custom and protected by law. Complaints usually met with heavy sarcasm, the unfailing weapon of the unassailable: 'the first, greatest, oldest and most respectable smoke – now an established institution, a vested interest, sweet to the palate of those who thrive by it'.[38] That existing anti-smoke legislation was even acknowledged in Swansea was a result of the persistence of one man: Dr William Henry Michael, the Borough's first medical officer of health.

Swansea-born, Michael began medical practice during the cholera epidemic of 1848–9. He was elected to the council in 1852, and in 1853 he became the town's first paid medical officer of health, having been its unpaid *de facto* officer for about a year. The Public Health Act of 1848 had enabled town councils to form local boards of health but the Swansea council, in spite of a cholera epidemic in 1847, waited two years before adopting the legislation. It took two more years to work out a scheme for obtaining and distributing untainted water, and only through Michael's insistence did the town get a healthy reservoir.

But as medical officer, Michael was continually frustrated by the intransigence of the Swansea Board of Health, in effect the town council, which ignored the directives of the Public Health Act. In 1855 Michael resigned as medical officer, reasoning that he could be more effective as an ordinary member of council and, by extension, of the Board of Health. He was duly reappointed to council – as medical officer he had been forced to resign his council seat – and in 1857 he was elected mayor. As mayor, he was one of Swansea's brightest and best, discharging his duties, particularly those on the justices' bench with, as one of his obituarists noted, 'skill, distinction, and humanity'. After his term as mayor he served as an alderman until 1861 and then took up the law, his true avocation. He became a distinguished QC.[39]

Michael's first and only chance to rid Swansea of some of its smoke came in the late 1850s. The Local Government Act of 1858, designed to remove the appearance of centralization in the administration of public health, incorporated some of the clauses of the Towns Improvement Act of 1847.[40] The clause in the new legislation that caught Michael's attention was the 108th section of the Towns Improvement Act. It stipulated that every furnace or fireplace built after the passing of the special Act (1858) should be so constructed as to consume the smoke arising from combustibles. Furnaces and fireplaces built before the Act and not so constructed were granted a two-year period of grace before having to be altered. The Act did not apply to the smelting of ores.[41]

In June 1859 Michael signalled his intention to bring before the notice of the Swansea Board of Health those parts of the Act that applied to the consumption of smoke from combustibles, and of his intention to move a resolution demanding compliance from local manufacturers.[42] Michael, surprisingly, was supported by the *Cambrian*, hitherto a hawkish defender of smoke. It censured the local board of health for having avoided the smoke question 'entirely up to this time', and appealed for prompt action to atone for its 'culpable procrastination in the past'.[43]

There were signs, too, of growing resistance to smoke in the community at large: a layer of opinion, formerly suppressed, was slowly surfacing. 'Spelter and Copper Smoked' from the Vale of Tawe wrote to the *Cambrian* complaining of Swansea council's fear of offending 'My Lord Copper'. The writer argued that it was quite absurd to reason that because Swansea had been a mere fishing village 150 years earlier it would have remained so without copper. What, he asked rhetorically, about Cardiff and Brighton?[44] Another correspondent, also anonymous, applauded W. H. Michael for 'standing alone against the nuisance'.

But not all critics took cover in anonymity. On discovering that Hussey Vivian had bought a defunct zinc spelter works at Morriston and intended relighting the furnaces as soon as trade improved, William Jowett wrote to the Local Government Act Office urging it to send an inspector to assess the effects of the smoke.[45] Earlier letters to Vivian had not been answered and Jowett saw no point in approaching the Swansea Board of Health whose members were, he feared, 'interested parties'. Jowett presented himself as a spokesman for the working man whose garden, rather than his home, was his castle. A collier or copperman might tolerate discomfort and inconvenience in the house but he resented having his garden assailed by 'poisonous sulphur smoke'. In his reponse to the Local Government Act Office Vivian pleaded his prescriptive right: he had not built the works, Morriston was already defiled and no remedy for the smoke problem was to hand.[46] To Jowett he wrote that his complaint was the first intimation he had that the spelter works was considered anything but a benefit to Morriston.[47] Bristling at this reponse from a powerful employer accustomed to hearing only soft answers, Jowett retorted stoutly that no doubt he was the first to complain, and for a patently obvious reason. 'Can any man employed by you or through you do so, without the risk of being dismissed . . . but apply the Ballot and then see how matters will stand.'[48] Offended by the tone of the letter, Hussey Vivian declined further correspondence.[49]

There was also resistance to copper smoke in Taibach. Where only a single works stood on an open, if narrow, coastal plain, the smoke problem was not nearly so acute as in the Tawe valley, but it offended both visitors and residents. Early guidebooks to south Wales were fond of describing the village as a long row of whitewashed cottages (the 'Constant') and a dense cloud of smoke. Even Hussey Vivian, in jocular mood, conceded that the smoke in Taibach went up not in volumes but in encyclopaedias. The most articulate of the complainants was the Reverend Richard Morgan (Rhydderch ap Morgan), Taibach's first historian. In 'Blodau Brynawen' (The Flowers of Brynawen) he attacked the smoke in a poem, six verses long, and in the following *englyn*, 'Mwg Gwaith Taibach' (Smoke from the Taibach Works), for which he won a prize at an eisteddfod in 1868:[50]

> Ammhuredd y mwg marwol – sy'n arwain
> Pwys ochain pesychol,
> Fe lyn i ladd dyn a dol,
> Ag anianawdd gwenwynol.

A literal translation reads: the poisonous and deadly nature of the fumes causes bronchial trouble and kills lake, man and meadow alike.

Although smoke from the burning of coal, not the smelting of copper, was the target of the 1858 Act, the copper industry was a massive user of coal and in Swansea it was impossible to proceed with legislation that might impinge in any way upon copper smelting. Word of Michael's proposal spread quickly through the town and in its wake followed a petition deploring both the threat it presented to the town's smelters and the advantage it would give to rivals in Liverpool and elsewhere. At a special meeting of the Board of Health the mayor, who clearly objected to the proposal, announced that there were 3,000 signatures on the petition, including those of 'very influential inhabitants', and several hundred on additional sheets of paper. He also declared that many of the signatories were landowners, not just merchants from Wind Street and Castle Street, and that this surely was proof that smoke was not as 'injurious to property as some other persons thought'. It was left to Michael to point out that most of the petitioners had direct connections with the copper trade and that there were fewer signatures on the petition than marks.[51]

In the hope of averting a confrontation between Michael and the Board, the town clerk for Swansea (C. B. Mansfield) had written at length to the Local Government Act Office to ask for clarification of the law, and for guidance as to what steps the local board might take to eliminate the nuisance complained of.[52] In his reply Tom Taylor, the new secretary of the Local Government Act Office, was ultra-cautious. The draft of his letter to Mansfield is a cat's cradle of deletions, insertions and after-thoughts. He knew how sensitive Swansea was to the smoke issue and, by virtue of his office, he was a defender of local autonomies. Embarrassed, too, by ambiguities in the law, he sidestepped the issue, pleading ignorance of the special circumstances of the district and advising the Board to proceed 'with a wise regard to industrial interests' and 'the prosperity of the district'.[53]

How direct an attack Michael intended on the copper works is not clear, and it is difficult to know whether an oblique approach would even have been possible; in nineteenth-century Swansea it was assumed that a debate about smoke, from no matter what source, was really a debate about copper smoke. But whatever Michael's intentions, he was drawn into a frontal attack by what he regarded as a venal attempt to distinguish between smoke and vapour. Hussey Vivian and Pascoe Grenfell had also written to the embattled Tom Taylor ostensibly seeking clarification of the law but in effect reminding him that the 108th clause in the Towns' Improvement Act applied only to the burning of combustibles: 'It must be borne in mind . . . that before the Legislature interfered it has never been proved practicable to smelt ores without vapours of an inconsumable character arising from them.'[54]

In his reply to Vivian and Grenfell, Taylor suggested a semantic defence by making a distinction between smoke and vapour. Smoke, he suggested, was the emission of fires and coal-burning furnaces, vapour or gases of smelters. Within the meaning of the Act, gases from smelters were not smoke at all.[55] Although the authors of Towns Improvement Clauses Act (1847) had, for the purposes of the law, attempted to distinguish between smelter and other smoke, Taylor's attempt to describe one set of emissions as smoke and the other as vapour offended the scientist in Michael. 'A more vapoury and empty distinction' he had never heard. By pointing out that all smoke, except for the incombustible particles, is vapour or gas, Michael destroyed Taylor's argument. And to the discomfiture of his opponents on the council he did so by citing John Henry Vivian's report to the Committee for the Fund for Obviating Copper Smoke. Vivian's opinions, as he would later characterize them before a select committee on noxious vapours, 'were not the mere theories of a chemist' but the 'decisive dicta of one who had spent his whole life in the prosecution of the smelting of copper and who, more than any other authority I know of, is worthy of being listened to'.[56]

But in the process of undermining Taylor's position and embarrassing his adversaries, Michael shifted the focus of the debate to copper smoke. He acknowledged that the Local Government Act applied only to coal smoke but he could not resist pointing out that sulphur, a constituent of most copper ores, was one of the most powerful combustibles known. He acknowledged, too, that in copper smelting it was impossible to separate the gases produced by coal and those by copper ore, but still he persisted with his motion. He pointed out that he demanded no more than had been promised twenty-five years earlier by John Henry Vivian. Hafod's culverts, showers and stacks had eliminated the incombustible particles and virtually all the gases except sulphurous acid gas, and their adoption had been 'earnestly recommended' to the copper masters by the then mayor (Dr J. C. Collins) and Corporation. The present Act demanded no more than Vivian's scheme had been able to deliver and, Michael contended, the Board would be neglecting its duty if, by doing nothing, it allowed the Act to become a dead letter.

Michael, of course, was tilting at windmills. There was a long pause before his seconder – presumably summoning his resources – responded to the resolution. The remaining Board members then fell upon the protagonists. E. M. Richards, probably the most outspoken defender of smoke, declared that Swansea had not enough smoke: 'They lived by smoke – they had thriven by smoke', and he had yet to learn that smoke was injurious either to human life or to property. Vegetation might have suffered but the real value of property had increased. If the Board so much as resolved to refer the resolution to a committee the news would echo around the mining and smelting world. Via the *Mining Journal*, which according to Richards reported the Board's every reference to smoke, the message would go to South America and to all places where copper ores were mined that it was dangerous for any new smelting works to come to Swansea. The Board, he trusted, would not commit so suicidal an act and would not let slip an opportunity to settle the smoke question once for all.

Others spoke in a similar vein. George Strick wished that Michael had founded his arguments on commercial fact, not scientific theory, and that he had not asked the Board to abandon its task of protecting the best interests of Swansea by seeking to turn the town into an experimental laboratory. Even Michael's former supporters deserted him. G. B. Stroud, who had stood by Michael in earlier meetings, now moved to the opposition, saying that Swansea, her resort days long over, dare not place any impediments in the way of manufacturing.

In his reply, Michael reassured the Board that no draconian measures were intended and that it was his purpose merely to remind the Board and the townspeople of their municipal responsibilities. Even if the resolution were not passed it would still be the responsibility of the Board to see that the law was not broken. With defeat inevitable, he made two parting shots: that it was impossible to settle the smoke question forever that day, and that it was complete nonsense to talk of driving industries away from Swansea. Where else would they go, the Act being operative everywhere? But no argument, even one as well reasoned as Michael's, would persuade the Board. Michael and his seconder, Eli James, supported the motion; the remaining twenty members of the Board met it with a firm negative.[57]

Undaunted by the rejection, Michael waited for the two-year period of grace granted by the 1858 Act to elapse before raising the subject again. In August 1860 he presented the Board with virtually the same resolution, but with the rider that manufacturers who had failed to comply with the 1858 Act be given a month's notice to do so. The *Cambrian*, his ally two years earlier, now scolded him for once again 'dragging' the smoke problem before the local parliament.[58] Although Michael, as he later testified to the Select Committee on Noxious Vapours (1862), thought he had all the argument on his side, all the votes went against him. The voting was twenty to four against the resolution. 'The Commissioners', he told the Select Committee, 'who are the town council ... would hardly be men likely to appreciate a scientific argument, or to look beyond present consequences' – the lament, now familiar, of conservationists everywhere. Because of the obstinacy of the local Board of Health, Michael advised the Select Committee that injuries to the public in Swansea were 'totally without remedy'.[59]

The difficulties of proceeding against smoke from any source, for fear of offending 'My Lord Copper', were demonstrated again by the fate of a second action against the Patent Fuel Co., and another against a centrally located brickworks. Feelings against the Fuel Company continued to run high and its owners might fairly have claimed that they were scapegoats for a community unwilling to tackle the problem of smoke on a broad front. After the 1852 action the company began to distil the naphtha from the coal tar, thus removing a chief cause of the nuisance, and it built an immense flue to carry the now cleaner smoke to the top of Kilvey Hill. The eminent metallurgist – and trained physician – Dr John Percy, a visitor to Swansea at the time of the dispute, wondered how a community that could 'submit without a murmur to the sulphureous and choking exhalations of the copper works' could become so agitated over patent fuel smoke.[60] The ambivalence found perfect expression in the person of Dr George Gwynne Bird. He could find nothing harmful or even offensive in copper smoke, but smoke from the Patent Fuel works was 'most beastly, horrible, and offensive to health'.[61]

But there was no ambivalence in the town council, the merchants and most of the professional men. They might tolerate complaints about smoke, but at the approach of the law they closed ranks and formed a phalanx around the manufacturers. At a public meeting convened at the Guildhall in December 1860 to deal with the latest injunction against the Patent Fuel Company, Dr Thomas Williams presented a motion – couched in an address that lasted three-quarters of an hour – that the injunction was 'highly detrimental to the commercial interests of this port'. He did, however, make the telling point that it was unfair to single out a works which had done everything in its power to suppress its smoke, while the copper works escaped censure. For Thomas Williams it was a bold statement, but he softened the blow by submitting to what John Percy described as a 'strange delusion'. He reiterated the sentiment, expressed in his report on copper smoke for the General Board of Health, that he had never encountered a single ailment that could be attributed to smoke of any kind. More than this, the 'entire absence' of typhus in the district could, he asserted, be attributed to the presence of copper and other smoke.[62]

At the request of the chairman of the meeting, W. H. Michael declared that when serving as a publicly appointed scientific assessor – in response to an indictment for public nuisance against the Patent Fuel Company – he found that the company had taken every reasonable measure to consume its smoke. On the strength of his assessment, the indictment had been withdrawn. He advised the meeting that in the case of an action for injury to private property it could not usurp the function of the courts, but that there was nothing to be lost by a public expression of support for the Patent Fuel Company. This, of course, the assembly readily granted.

Seven years later the threat of an injunction against a Swansea brick-works triggered a similar closing of ranks. Through an extraordinary provision of the 1866 Sanitary Act, any person, by complaining to the Home Secretary, could compel a local board of health to perform any of its statutory duties. Upon request, the Home Secretary would send an inspector to investigate the cause of complaint and if the inspector discovered that the local board had been negligent the Home Secretary could enforce the statute. By a stroke of the pen, as the historian Robert Gutchen pointed out, the permissive powers of local authorities had been turned into compulsory ones.[63] *The Times* saw in the Act a great victory for the cause of public health: 'Instead of option we have obligation, and instead of the will and pleasure of Town-councillors, we now have the law of the land.'[64]

In other towns this particular provision of the Sanitary Act had galvanized hitherto lackadaisical authorities, but in Swansea it had no power to move, the local board of health stirring only when it perceived a threat to the commercial interests of the town. In the late summer of 1867 Lieutenant Colonel Morgan, of the Royal Glamorgan Artillery Militia, complained to the Home Secretary that the Swansea Board of Health had ignored his request to invoke the Local Government Act relating to the burning of combustibles.[65] Coal smoke mixed with fume from the baking of salt-impregnated clay from a nearby brickworks poured over the armouries. The complaint prompted a letter from the Home Secretary's Office to the Swansea Board of Health asking what action it intended to take. The 'meddlers', as Gabriel Powell might have put it, were knocking on the municipal doors. The letter created consternation in the Board. At its monthly meeting, Councillor J. T. Jenkins of Morriston declared that it would be 'a very sorry day for Swansea when the Act of Parliament was put into practical operation'. He pointed out that it was 'a very delicate thing' to single out a particular works, for once the process of identifying culprits had begun where would it end? All smoke trails in Swansea, of course, led back to the copper works. He thought that Colonel Morgan had acted in bad grace by threatening the very people who had accommodated the militia in the first place; the armouries were built on land leased from the brickworks.

Jenkins also reminded the Board that when the question of implementing anti-smoke legislation had been discussed previously, out of a full Board of twenty-four members only two (W. H. Michael and Eli James) had voted in favour of doing so. He moved that the Board take no action on the question of brickworks smoke, but more astute members pointed out that this would merely be to invite the attentions of a Home Office inspector. Instead, it was suggested that the brickworks, for the sake of appearances, be asked to build a small, inexpensive – and by definition ineffectual – stack. In the end, however, the Board opted for a political solution; as a demonstration of concern sufficient, it was hoped, to keep Home Office watchdogs at bay, it decided to send a letter to the brickworks that merely inquired about the steps it intended to take to abate the nuisance.[66]

In its determination not to touch smoke from any source, the Swansea Board received the tacit approval of the Local Government Act Office. In other towns the Office had acted promptly to correct alleged defaults by municipal authorities. At Henley, the *Cambrian* reported in September 1865, the local board of health 'woke up' and dealt with a smoke nuisance after an official investigation. But in the case of Swansea, the Local Government Act Office was reluctant to intervene. In a private letter to Tom Taylor, the director of the Office, Robert Rawlinson of the Rivers commission noted that copper and other 'deleterious fumes' had turned the Swansea valley into 'a monster nuisance district' that seemed to be without remedy.[67] Fear of damaging the copper industry had made the Local Government Act Office very cautious in its handling of

Swansea's affairs and it had no interest in overriding local considerations merely for the sake of a more centralized system of government. In its gingerly correspondence with the Swansea Board of Health it limited the discussion to technical and scientific means of reducing brickworks smoke, ignoring the larger cloud that lay further up the valley.

At the end of 1868 Colonel Morgan and the Glamorgan Militia, weary of addressing a foe as evasive as a local board of health determined not to act, and a central authority just as determined not to intervene, gave up the struggle. 'The brickworks smoke', wrote Colonel Morgan in his final letter to the Home Office, 'is as intolerable as ever.'[68] In Swansea, as William Henry Michael had testified to the Noxious Vapours Committee, all smoke came under the protective wing of the copper industry and enjoyed *de facto* immunity from prosecution. A letter to the *Cambrian* summed up the dilemma. 'Why', asked its author, 'should the presence of the copper smoke mean that we are helpless to every other form of nuisance?'[69]

7

The Nedd Valley Disputes

◈

So thorough was the defeat of the Llansamlet farmers at the Carmarthen and Brecon trials that for twenty-five years no Glamorgan farmer or landowner would have considered it worthwhile to confront the copper-smelting interests. The earl of Jersey won concessions from Pascoe Grenfell and John Williams, of Williams, Foster & Co., but these appear to have been so small as to be hardly worth reporting.[1] The smelters seemed unassailable and no farmer could have proceeded against them with any expectation of success. W. H. Michael's testimony to the Select Committee on Noxious Vapours in May 1862 was a tale of inaction and even regression. The Swansea smelters, he asserted, made no effort to reduce either the amount of the smoke or its toxicity and such measures as had been taken earlier were long abandoned. 'They [the smelters] care nothing and do nothing.'[2] But in Swansea there were also practical reasons for the general inaction. Lands downwind of the works in the Tawe valley had been so badly damaged that, as Michael himself acknowledged, there was little incentive either to suppress the smoke or disperse it.

On discovering that none of their neighbours intended adopting long flues, shower chambers and tall stacks, the Vivians abandoned their own system on grounds that any good that they might have done would have been offset by the smoke from neighbouring works. High stacks, too, the Hafod furnacemen claimed, increased the draught to levels that drew copper particles up the chimneys and made control of the fires difficult. Nor, as the Llansamlet farmers had testified, were high stacks an answer to the problem of dispersing the smoke in enclosed valleys. Only at Pembrey and Llanelli, where the coast was flat and the river open-mouthed, were they still in use. At Pembrey a double-walled stack 271 feet high not only dispersed the smoke but did so, it was said, without interfering with the operation of the furnaces.[3] R. J. Nevill's 'Stac Fawr' at his Llanelli works was a towering 360 feet. At Llanelli, Nevill also persisted with water treatments, passing the smoke through chambers filled with absorbent 'clinkers', or slag, kept wet by water percolating through the roof. The treatment did not impede the draught and was so effective that corn and vegetables could now be grown near the works, allowing the Nevills to rent farms that earlier they had been obligated to buy because they were so badly damaged by copper smoke.[4] Nevill, too, made an effort to keep Llanelli as free as possible of waste tips by using the slag and ashes to make road beds and sea walls.

To raise the banner of agriculture east of the Llwchwr required the confidence, and possibly insouciance, of a well-to-do outsider. In the 1850s a standard-bearer appeared in the form of a Birmingham land agent and surveyor named Dugdale Houghton. From his father, John Houghton, he had inherited the Fforchdwm estate on Blaen Pelena, an isolated watershed between the Nedd and Afan river systems about five miles east of the town of Neath. To this day no main roads pass near Blaen Pelena and unclassified roads peter out before it can be reached. John Houghton bought the estate in 1816 following his appointment as clerk to the newly incorporated Neath Canal Company, and when he died, in 1825, he left the property to his five sons. Although the property produced some coal, the land itself was rough and only one of the sons, Dugdale, showed any interest in it.[5]

About 1850 Dugdale Houghton, then a middle-aged widower, decided to divide his life between his business in Birmingham and his estate in Wales. At Blaen Pelena he threw himself into the role of an English-style country landowner. He rebuilt one of the two farmhouses on the property, converting a simple upland dwelling into what was later described as a 'good residence', with three sitting rooms and seven bedrooms, and then gave his attention to land and stock.[6] For twenty-five years the estate had produced only coal and rough grazing. He bought cattle, sheep, horses and a few Jersey cows, and planted more than 300 acres with oak, larch and scotch fir. In 1853 he also bought the leases, and much of the stock, of three other farms, Coed yr Iarll Uchaf (Upper Earlswood), Coed yr Iarll Isaf (Lower Earlswood) and Cwrt y Bettws, near the mouth of the Nedd. In November 1856 the servants from all four farms, about fifty in all, sat down to a harvest supper of roast and boiled beef, ale and plum pudding that was followed by dancing until midnight to the strains of harp and violin. The evening ended with the singing of 'Success to the Plough' and 'To our Next Merry Meeting'.[7]

Dugdale Houghton versus Red Jacket

Beneath the two upland farms near the mouth of the Nedd, Coed yr Iarll Uchaf and Isaf, lay what proved to be the worm in Houghton's rural idyll: the recently built (1849) Red Jacket copper works. When Houghton acquired the leases of the farms, the owners of the Red Jacket works, directed by Professor Richard Phillips, had recently finished experimenting with a newly patented 'wet' or 'liquid' method of separating copper from its ore. In the 'wet' system high-grade pyritic ores from Cuba were calcined for twenty-four hours, mixed with salt, roasted again and then emptied into vats of water. The copper dissolved to produce a solution of copper sulphate that was then run through a series of 'precipitating' vats filled with iron plates or pieces of broken cast iron. Iron is attractive to copper held in solution. To harvest the copper, deposits were brushed from the broken iron and scraped from the plates.[8]

The 'wet' process was effective. It produced copper that was remarkably malleable and pure, and by reducing the number of calcinations and eliminating smelting, it did so by making far less smoke than the traditional 'dry' processes. But it turned out to be prohibitively expensive. Before calcining, the ores had to be ground under millstones and when being processed the heavy, bulky material had to be moved several times. After a trial period of about eight months the owners (Bankart and Sons) gradually reverted to the old, 'dry' methods of calcining and smelting and at the same time increased the number of furnaces and chimneys. The complete reversal coincided roughly with Houghton's lease of the Coed yr Iarll farms. In 1853, when Houghton took over the farms, there were about a dozen furnaces finished and two or three still being built. Smoke from the new calciners, driven by westerly winds funnelling through the Jersey Marine gap, the Nedd's pre-glacial – and now abandoned – estuary, bore down on the north-west face of Coed yr Iarll hill. It destroyed both animals and crops. Houghton brought an action for damages, the case coming before the Carmarthen Summer Assizes in July 1858.

The contestants made an odd pairing. Houghton was a businessman turned farmer and Frederick Bankart a solicitor (from London) turned copper smelter. Houghton's counsel, the Swansea-born William Grove, was far better known as a scientist than as a barrister, even though as the latter he had come into the public eye by assisting for the defence in the notorious Dr Palmer poison case.[9] As the inventor of the Grove (voltaic) Cell (1839), author of the celebrated *Correlation of Physical Forces* (1846) and a Fellow of the Royal Society, Grove was well known in scientific circles. He would be elected president of the Royal Society in 1866, five years before his elevation to the bench and six before the award of a knighthood.[10]

At Carmarthen, Grove was a model counsel and Houghton a model plaintiff. Houghton, the lead witness, explained how he had been attracted to the Coed yr Iarll farms by their suitability for raising stock, horses in particular. The pastures, a mixture of white clover and short

With a few well-chosen paragraphs, Grove had disarmed the defence's chief witness. A man less confident than Thomas Williams might have faltered but, unshaken, he asked if Grove intended to examine him on the entire book, and continued with his testimony. The report of the trial contains no summary of the directions given by the judge, Sir Charles Crompton, to the jury, but a reference to his castigation of the defence counsel for burdening the court with bulky documents extraneous to the case ('so much rubbish'), suggests that they could not have been favourable to the Bankarts. Although the trial had lasted three days the jurors retired for a mere half-hour. They returned with a verdict for the plaintiff, and an award of damages for £450. Sir Charles Crompton refused leave to move for a new trial or to entertain a plea for reduced damages. It was the country's first victory over the town.

The Bankarts were no more successful later in 1858 when they applied to the Master of the Rolls for an injunction to restrain Houghton from executing the Carmarthen verdict, or from taking further legal action. They contended that Houghton had taken the farm in full knowledge of the effects of copper smoke. Houghton in reply argued that new calcining furnaces had converted a process (the 'wet' process) that was virtually harmless into one that destroyed his pastures, crops and stock. The Master of the Rolls replied, judiciously, that the fact of the defendant's acquiescence in the works when they did him little or no injury ought not to deprive him of all remedy when by their increase he sustained serious damage. He could see no grounds for interfering with the previous judgment.[15]

The Trial at Swansea

After his success at Carmarthen and the rejection of the Bankarts' appeal, Houghton assumed that either the patent liquid process would be reinstated, or the stacks raised and some effort made to disperse the smoke, or the works moved to another place. None of the above occurred. Instead, the works was enlarged, the number of furnaces increased (to twenty-four), and the standard calcining and smelting processes continued. Houghton sued again, the action coming before the Glamorgan Summer Assizes, Swansea, in July 1860. Given the favourable Carmarthen verdict, and even greater emissions of smoke from the Red Jacket works, the Swansea trial ought to have been a formality. During the previous year, too, Houghton had received £1,200 in damages from the Briton Ferry Copper Works (built in 1853) for injuries to Cwrt y Bettws farm. At the Swansea trial William Grove, who was again the prosecuting counsel, opened quietly and carefully. He explained that Houghton, having reached that stage of life when business became onerous, looked to a 'quiet, easy, and comfortable residence' in south Wales. Here he fondly imagined – until his plans were thwarted by the Bankarts – that he would spend the rest of his days. In fact, he spent few of his days at Coed yr Iarll or Cwrt y Bettws, and less than half of the year in south Wales. Houghton's farming methods Grove described as 'most excellent' and 'far superior to anything which had been seen in that neighbourhood before'.[16]

The farms themselves were not only fertile but, overlooking Swansea Bay, beautifully and delightfully situated. In closing his address, however, Grove dropped a bombshell. He estimated Houghton's losses between 1856 and 1859 to have been more than £8,000. At the Carmarthen trial, in 1858, the claim for damages over a similar period was £864. Singular items on the new list were injuries to ferns (£175), loss of the beneficial and healthful use of his dwelling (£550), and losses due to the destruction of rabbits (£65).

Houghton's testimony was the by now standard litany of damage to crops and stock: how corn touched by the smoke looked as if it had been struck by lightning; how turnip leaves turned from dark green to yellow, and how the leaves, when rubbed, turned to powder. He also explained his claim for damages to rabbits. A large rabbit warren in the burrows on the channel side of the lower farm had been destroyed by copper smoke. Rabbits, then, were an important source of meat and commercial warrens were common. Houghton, who had sent rabbits to the Birmingham market in the previous four years was now unable to do so because the rabbits had become thin and their flesh had turned yellow. In the trade they were known as 'copper-smoke rabbits'.

When cross-examined by Montague Chambers, chief counsel for the defence, Houghton made the surprising admission that he could not name the owner of the Coed yr Iarll Isaf farm. He believed his solicitor, Mr Coke – to whom he paid the rent – was also his landlord, but he was not sure. The judge opined that it was a 'droll' man indeed who did not know the landlord of a farm where he claimed to have about £10,000 worth of property. For Houghton, the lapse was the beginning of the end of his case.

William Herepath and W. H. Michael appeared again for Houghton; both were convincing but neither offered new testimony. Of the lay witnesses, the most combative was Rees Prees, who had farmed Coed yr Iarll Isaf from 1816 to 1850, and his family for generations before that. Prees had also appeared at Carmarthen where he had bridled at the accusation that he was a retired man with nothing better to do than hang around the Coed yr Iarll farms. At Swansea he described how the property had deteriorated after the building of the Red Jacket works. In 1853 the farms had not suffered at all, but in 1854 ferns began to wither, quickset hedges die and crops of wheat crumple up. When cross-examined by Montague Chambers, Prees said that he *knew* rather than *thought* that the damage had been done entirely by copper smoke from Red Jacket. To the insinuation that he was a paid witness he replied stoutly that he was in no man's pocket, neither that of the learned counsel nor of anyone else. Chambers he clearly disliked. In his testimony he referred to a horse that had drowned on Coed yr Iarll in a place where the learned counsel might also have come to grief because the horse had fallen in by its head.

In the hands of Montague Chambers, the defence at Swansea was far tighter than it had been at Carmarthen, and it had an obvious weakness to exploit: the amount claimed for damages. To demand damages of £8,000 over three years for farms that rented for £240 annually was the worst case of 'cooking the accounts' that he (Montague Chambers) had ever experienced. Houghton, who as a land agent specialized in railway compensation cases, had clearly mistaken his calling. Instead of turning to farming in Wales he ought to have been returned for Birmingham in place of Mr Bright, the then Chancellor of the Exchequer. Had he done so then the entire country might have benefited from his financial wizardry. Adventurers to the goldfields of Australia and California might also have saved themselves time and trouble by staying at home and making gold from copper in Briton Ferry.

Chambers turned next to the question of individual responsibility. He declaimed, as had Sir James Scarlett at the first copper-smoke trial, that in any civilized society private sacrifices must be made for the public good. The defendants' works, on the bank of a river and in a locality served by a canal and two railways, were carried on in a fit place and in a fit and proper manner, and who could deny their benefit to the community. As a new enterprise in the Nedd valley, Red Jacket could not claim a prescriptive right to smelt copper, but Houghton, a man of broad experience, had rented the Coed yr Iarll farms with his eyes open and in full knowledge of the effects of copper smoke upon vegetation. He had assured Howard Bankart, manager of the Red Jacket works and son of the defendant, that by manuring and good farming practices he could offset the effects of the smoke and make the farms productive. Not only this, but in 1859 Houghton had renewed his lease of the farms for a further fourteen years. In doing so had he not tacitly admitted that no serious damage was being done?

To counter the testimony of Houghton and Rees Prees, Montague

Chambers called a number of farm witnesses. Mary Bowen, who had lived on Coed yr Iarll Uchaf farm for nineteen years before her husband's death in 1847, thought the farm unsuitable for the superior kind of horses that Houghton liked to breed, adding that the Jersey Marine burrows were too exposed even for hardy Welsh ponies. C. H. Smith, a magistrate of the county and a farmer in Llansamlet, testified that he had farmed successfully for thirty years by not keeping his animals for more than two years and by keeping them away from damp ground, especially in winter. The rapid turnover, he insisted, was made necessary by the poverty of the soil – which was common to the district – not by copper smoke. Richard Thomas, who farmed within a quarter of a mile of the Vivians' works at Taibach, declared that copper smoke had neither killed nor injured any of his stock. Thomas, however, was clearly compromised. When cross-examined he revealed that he was an agent for the Cwmafan copper works and that his duties were to settle claims against the company. Equally compromised was Charles Henry Waring, owner of land and coal mines in Neath Abbey, who testified that his horses had never been harmed by copper smoke. When examined by the prosecuting counsel he was forced to admit that he supplied coal and leased land to the Mines Royal copper works.

With the Carmarthen trial behind them, the Bankarts no longer denied that copper smoke damaged crops and stock, but they refused to concede that they were liable for damages. On this point they had declined the judge's pre-trial request that the dispute be settled by arbitration instead of by costly trial. The Bankarts' entire case rested, as Montague Chambers pointed out in his closing address, on the assertion that the works was located in a fit and proper place and that in a well-ordered state the rights and privileges of individuals must yield to the general interests of trade and commerce. Dugdale Houghton, averred Chambers, could hardly complain of a nuisance when he had come to the nuisance with his eyes open. When he looked at the Coed yr Iarll farms he must have seen the smoke coming over them, and by taking a lease had he not, in effect, granted leave and license to the copper works. Finally, and tellingly, he declared that Houghton could never have sustained anything like the damages he alleged. The plaintiff's claims were, he contended, 'of the most exorbitant character ever brought into a court of justice'.

Grove countered with the argument that the location of the works was neither convenient nor proper, and that there were many acres in the Tawe valley, already spoiled beyond repair, where the works could have been built. He also contested the defence's claim that the works had been carried on in a way least likely to harm surrounding farmland. Not only had the Bankarts abandoned the wet method of processing but they had not even built tall stacks. In his testimony W. H. Michael had pointed out that a high chimney and long culverts could have reduced the damage in the vicinity of the works; the Red Jacket stacks were low, a standard 50 feet. Finally, and perhaps unwisely before a Swansea jury, Grove asked the jurors to place themselves in the plaintiff's position. Supposing they had chosen a pleasant farm, beautifully situated and of most luxuriant foliage, and there had fondly hoped to pass the remainder of their days. Supposing, too, they had laid out capital and farmed in a most up-to-date way only to find that smoke from a neighbouring works thwarted their efforts by destroying the vegetation and creating a veritable desert. This was the plaintiff's position and if every farthing he asked for were granted, Grove asserted, it would not be too much.

It remained for the judge, Sir George Bramwell, to mediate between the two positions. His instructions to the jury were unequivocal. There could be no doubt that copper smoke damaged crops and stock. This had been admitted so forthrightly by Mr Bankart that he (Justice Bramwell) had considered halting the trial on grounds that the action was unde-fended. The injuries to the plaintiff's crops and stock, therefore, could be justified only if it could be shown that the works had to be where they were. Unlike the Swansea smelters, the Bankarts could not claim any right gained by antiquity, customary usage or prescription. The works had been built only ten years previously. Everything hinged, therefore, on whether, in legal terminology, the works was in a convenient place, or a fit and proper place. Next to a navigable river, a canal and a railway, the location was uncommonly convenient for the Bankarts. But was it convenient for Houghton? It struck Justice Bramwell as a matter of common sense that Mr Bankart might have chosen to locate his works along the Tawe where it could have done no additional harm. Damages, clearly, were due the plaintiff and the only question remaining was to determine the amount or the 'quantum' sustained.

It was on this issue that Houghton's case collapsed. Justice Bramwell, as had Montague Chambers, considered Houghton's claim to be outlandish: 'most extravagant', 'enormously exaggerated' or 'rank'. A 'rank' case was one where the damages were set so high that the defen-dants had little prospect of being able to pay. He regarded Grove's attempt to reduce the amount of the claim during the trial as being a case of too little too late, and intimated that Grove had acted only because he sensed his (the judge's) displeasure. The plaintiff actually sought to be repaid three times over: first he claimed for his rent; second for his losses on the land; and third for what he had paid to supply his losses. Was not this nonsense?

Justice Bramwell agreed with the witness Mrs Bowen that to attempt to raise high-breed carriage and riding horses on a Welsh hillside and in coastal burrows was asking too much of nature, and he advised that these particular claims for damages be dismissed. The claim for rabbits he thought unworthy of a single observation. It was, he said, 'simply nonsense' to make such a claim. Ferns, too, got equally short shrift. The judge was no farmer but even he knew that at best they were used for bedding, and had not a highly respectable witness testified that they were worth only 5 shillings a ton!

But his true displeasure the judge reserved for the larger monetary claims. The claim for injuries to grass stripped him of all judicial restraint. 'Could anybody in his senses believe that, unassisted in any way, a farm let at 180 pounds a year would produce grass to the value of 900 pounds', or, expressed areally, 'let at two shillings and fourpence an acre would yield a pound an acre'. Such a thing, he expostulated, 'was preposterous – downright nonsense'. A legal case, like a man, is known by the company it keeps, and such outrageous claims, the judge felt bound to remark, made him deeply suspicious of the character of the whole. He concluded that no man ever lost so much in his life from farms of this size. Never in his experience had he seen a case of one-tenth part so extravagant a nature.

After such a summing up, Houghton might have counted himself lucky to get a penny. The jurors retired for an hour and a quarter and on their return awarded him damages of £150, one-fiftieth of the amount requested and less than half of the amount awarded at Carmarthen. When asked by the judge if they thought the Bankarts' operation had been carried on in a proper place and in a fit and proper manner they remained silent.

The costs of the Swansea trial appear to have drained Houghton's resources; in 1862 he informed his lawyer that he had £800–£900 worth of antiques in pawn. The result of the trial also dampened his enthusiasm for farming in south Wales. He left in 1868, but with sufficient funds to buy a mansion house, Dowles Manor, in Worcestershire. Yet in spite of his troubled sojourn in Wales he left some of his heart in Blaen Pelena. His tombstone is inscribed 'formerly of Fforchdwm near Neath, S.W.'.[17]

Nash Vaughan and the Rheola Estate

Within three years of the second Houghton/Bankart trial, copper smoke was again an issue in the Neath district. In May 1863 a group of landowners, concerned about the future of the valley, met at Neath's Castle Hotel. Their purpose was to form an association bent on saving from destruction a 'hitherto beautiful and fertile district'. The enemy was copper smoke and the association resolved to coerce local coppermasters into doing everything possible to suppress it. To assuage Swansea interests, the convener of the meeting, Nash Edwards Vaughan MP, let it be known that neither he nor his associates had any intention of pursuing Swansea smelters. Their arena was the Nedd valley where they believed there was still hope of salvaging land and scenery. The Tawe valley where, as Nash Vaughan remarked, 'all possible injury to vegetation had long since been committed', they regarded as a lost cause.[18]

In spite of Vaughan's reassurances, the *Cambrian* inveighed against him and his associates for fomenting discontent that could so easily end in vexatious litigation. It reminded them that trade as well as property had rights and submitted that long-established works and the prosperity of an entire district ought not to be threatened by a group of disgruntled landowners: 'Mr Vaughan's pet Association'. The association's true concern, it insinuated, was less the welfare of the valley than 'a few [blighted] trees . . . on a gentleman's estate'.[19] The estate in question was Rheola, a 6,000-acre property that stretched northward from the Gnoll to encompass much of the Nedd valley. Bought by John Edwards from Lady Molly Mackworth and her husband Capel Hanbury Leigh, it was considered the showpiece of what was then a many-jewelled valley – by general consent the loveliest in south Wales. Rheola house, about half-way up the valley, was enlarged by the distinguished architect John Nash, designer of Regent Street, Buckingham Palace and the Oriental Pavilion at Brighton. Nash was both a friend to John Edwards and his grandson's namesake.[20]

Nash Vaughan's interest in copper smoke, as explained in a letter to *The Times*, in September 1865, had been triggered by his membership of a committee charged with the reassessment of poor and county rates in Glamorgan.[21] Around Swansea and Neath the valuation of hundreds of acres of farmland had to be reduced by half; on these lands young stock could not be raised at all, and cows and horses kept on smoke-affected grasses soon died of 'salivation'. Even his own estate, which was several miles from the nearest copper works, had been affected. When a 300-acre woodland began 'pining' for no apparent reason, he sent parts of the trees to a well-known analytical chemist in London. In them the chemist found traces of sulphuric acid and recognizable quantities of arsenic. The only possible sources were copper works at the mouth of the river Nedd or further along the coast in Cwmafan and Taibach. Using estimates of damage to his own estate, and the evidence of the assessments, Vaughan calculated that more than 20,000 acres of woodland and farmland in the neighbourhood of Swansea and Neath were undergoing slow poison by copper smoke. In the letter he also noted that in thirty-five years the coppermasters, protected by law, had done nothing to mitigate the effects of the smoke.

Disturbed by the general decline in the value of assessments, and by the particular damage to his own property, Nash Vaughan decided to act. He was instrumental in forming the Nedd valley landowners' association, and in 1866 he brought an action against the English Copper Company in Cwmafan for injuries to the Rheola estate. His decision to prosecute followed an announcement, by Hussey Vivian in 1865, of an invention that finally enabled copper smelters to rid the smoke of sulphurous gases. With a remedy to hand, they could no longer hide behind the skirts of the law.

Metallurgists and chemists had long been convinced that the only real hope of eliminating sulphur from copper smoke lay in converting it into sulphuric acid. When Michael Faraday was first confronted with the problem of removing sulphurous gases from the smoke, his immediate response had been: 'Don't let them escape.' The difficulty lay in the means. By passing the smoke through horizontal cylinders filled with heated clinkers coated with sesquoxide of iron, Alfred Trueman of the 'Spitty' works had been able (c.1850) to convert sulphurous gases into sulphuric acid. But the method worked only under experimental conditions; as a commercial or factory process, as Thomas Williams noted at the first Houghton/Bankart trial, it did not serve.

The first patented design to trap copper smoke and condense the sulphurous gases was the invention of Thomas Bell in 1846. Bell experimented with a three-bedded calciner in which heat from the fuel travelled upward through the beds of ore, gathering sulphurous gases as it rose. From the calciner the fume passed via a long flue into a roasting kiln filled with large pieces of copper ore, and finally into sulphuric acid chambers or condensers. Powerful steam jets used to maintain the draught of the calciner and the kiln also provided water for the condensing process.

Though ingenious, Bell's condensers were not particularly effective, and to reduce the amount of smoke entering them Bell substituted anthracite, coke or charcoal for bituminous coal. The substitution increased the costs of calcining and there were no takers for his patent as a result. He approached John Williams, of Williams, Foster and Co. of Swansea, but his offer was refused. The law – as Bell remarked – was so weak and the profits from smelting so great that there was no incentive to increase them by manufacturing sulphuric acid.[22]

The weakness of Bell's process was that it allowed fuel smoke and fume from the ore to mix, thus necessitating the use of a relatively smokeless fuel. About fifteen years after seeing Bell's experiments in Newcastle upon Tyne, a Manchester chemist, Peter Spence, addressed the problem of separating fuel smoke from fume. Spence built a long calcining furnace, 40 or 50 feet from end to end, divided into two chambers: a lower one for fuel and an upper one for ore. He divided the chambers with a thin layer of firebrick. Smoke from the fire escaped via a chimney at the far end of the chamber, never contacting fume from the ore. The ore, introduced at the cool, far end of the furnace, was gradually drawn toward the fire, heating and giving off sulphur as it moved. To speed the calcining, he introduced a current of hot air which, in rising above the ore, also served to drive the fume through apertures in the wall of the furnace into adjacent sulphuric acid chambers. In these the gases were concentrated and condensed. Spence's process, patented in 1861, and blessed by both the *Mining Journal* and Dr John Percy, appears to have worked but it, too, was never adopted by the industry.[23]

Britain, in mid-century, produced yet a third patent for removing sulphur from copper smoke. To eliminate the need for the special furnaces, kilns, condensing chambers and steam boilers, required by both the Bell and Spence patents, Dr A. Gurlt of Birmingham patented a scheme for converting sulphurous acid gas into free sulphur rather than sulphuric acid. He channelled the smoke – shades of Bevington Gibbins – through a red-hot layer of carbonaceous material that could be anthracite, coal, coke or simply waste fuel from the smelting furnaces. On leaving the firegrate the gases were cooled – reducing the sulphur to its solid state – and then forced by a fan through bags or sacks of permeable cloth in which the flowers of sulphur accumulated. The advantage of Gurlt's process was that it could be applied to existing furnaces, and it yielded a product that could be sold more cheaply than acid and transported more easily. It also dispensed with the need for tall chimneys because the draught could be created mechanically.[24]

Yet in spite of its apparent advantages, Gurlt's process was never applied on a commercial scale. The Grenfells experimented with firegrates, cooling pipes and filters but they did not adopt them. The winning patent, in the sense that it was the only one to be taken up by the industry, was the invention of a German metallurgist, Moritz Gerstenhofer. Like the Bell and the Spence patents, Gerstenhofer's also required special furnaces and condensing chambers, but instead of separating the coal and the ore, as in Spence's furnace, it dispensed altogether with the need for coal by using the sulphur itself as fuel.

A Gerstenhofer furnace was a high rectangular chamber filled with rows of bars so arranged that no two bars in succeeding rows were directly above one another. The ore, finely divided, was introduced from the top and tumbled slowly to the bottom of the furnace; feed rollers in the roof of the furnace regulated the supply. On the sides of the furnace between the feed rolls and the bars were apertures through which the fume could escape. To begin calcination a fire was lit in a grate below the bars and the ore fed in from above. As soon as the sulphur began to burn, the firegrate was withdrawn and the burning encouraged by a draught of forced air. Once calcined, the ore was withdrawn from the bottom of the furnace and the fume driven by forced air into lead-lined condensing chambers where it was converted into sulphuric acid.[25] Through 'arte', as the Elizabethan apprentice George Nedham might have put it, one of copper's 'most hurtfull enemyes', had been made a 'friende'.

On learning of the invention from B. G. Herrmann, Hafod's German chemist, Hussey Vivian promptly bought the patent; he and Herrmann had been fellow students at the Mining Institute of the University of Freiburg, John Henry Vivian's alma mater. Hussey Vivian and Herrmann swore by the Gerstenhofer process. In a letter to Nash Vaughan, written in June 1865, Vivian noted that they had tested two of the new calciners over several months and, satisfied with the results, they were building twenty-six others at the Hafod and Taibach works. By 1868 only four of the old calciners remained at Hafod. The new condensers were large lead-lined structures about 100 feet high, 30 feet long and 25 feet wide. At Hafod, where they were built on the flattened tops of slag heaps, they towered above the works.

Hussey Vivian declared the 'novel and beautiful' process to be 'a perfect success', and predicted that it would eliminate most of the toxic vapours issuing from their calcining and roasting furnaces.[26] He estimated that at Hafod and Taibach about two-thirds of the vapours were condensed and turned to profitable account. Some of the acid was sold to local tinplate works, where it was used in the pickling or cleaning process, and the rest used in the manufacture of chemicals. By a supreme irony, one of the marketable by-products of a gas so destructive of soil and vegetation was superphosphate, a valuable fertilizer. When treated with sulphuric acid imported phosphate rock, which was brought directly to the Hafod wharves, became superphosphate fertilizer, 'Vivian's manures'. In a speech to a meeting of the West Glamorgan Agricultural Association, Hussey Vivian, hitherto the scourge of farmers, declared mischievously that it amused him to have found a way of making fertilizer from a herbicide. From smoke he could now make corn – 'ex fumo dare cerem'.[27]

For Nash Vaughan, Vivian's endorsement of the Gerstenhofer condensers gave him the legal leverage he needed against the English

Copper Company. Now that a way had been found of cleaning the smoke, the company was no longer protected at law. In September 1865 a *Times* article on Vivian's patent prompted several letters to the editor, one from an old Swansea copperman who proposed that the time was now ripe to apply the provisions of the Alkali Act to copper works. In 1862 a select committee of the House of Lords, appointed to investigate emissions of noxious vapours from manufacturing works, had concluded that emissions from alkali works – where common salt was treated with sulphuric acid – could easily be controlled but emissions from copper works, though they could be mitigated, still eluded the powers of science and technology.

Vaughan's action against the English Copper Company was scheduled for the Glamorgan Summer Assizes, Swansea, 1866, but the company, anticipating defeat in the courts, capitulated before the hearing.[28] It agreed to take all reasonable measures, consistent with smelting processes, to suppress the smoke, and if after two years Vaughan or his tenants were not satisfied with the results they could appeal to the Board of Trade. The Board would then appoint a referee with powers – should they be needed – to assess damages.[29]

Although forced to install Gerstenhofer condensers, the English Copper Company could scarcely have been charged with negligence. To protect the enclosed Cwmafan valley from copper smoke, it had commissioned the designer of the Cwmafan works, the Scottish engineer William Brunton, to build a culvert that would channel smoke from the furnaces in the bottom of the valley to a stack on the summit of Mynydd y Foel, 1,200 feet above sea level. Brunton's culvert was a stone arch, 15 feet wide, 11 feet high and a mile long, that at intervals was interrupted by low stone walls built diagonally across the tunnel to trap the copper particles in the smoke. From the Etna-like summit, sea winds carried the smoke away from the neighbourhood of the works.[30] But in copper-smelting country all winds are ill winds and tall stacks, as the Llansamlet farmers had learned thirty years earlier, merely extended their range. Valleys are natural air funnels so smoke that might have sailed harmlessly over Port Talbot drifted up the Nedd to settle on the Rheola estate.

With the English Copper Company's capitulation, farmers and landowners had finally gained a substantial victory. But it proved hollow. Nash Vaughan, who had been ill for some time, died at Inchbar, Ross-shire, in 1868 and a few years later the English Copper Company dismantled its condensers. In spite of Hussey Vivian's claims for the effectiveness of the condensers, neither fellow copper smelters nor the mining and metal fraternity shared his enthusiasm for them.[31] September 1865 saw a series of articles in the *Mining Journal* sceptical of his patent and critical of his 'somewhat hasty agitation' in urging it upon others. It accused Vivian of urging local landowners to harass the smelters so that they might be persuaded to buy the Vivian patent. Swansea people, declared the *Journal*, were naïve to think that the patent would not increase the costs of production. The ore had to be finely crushed in order to travel through the bars and burn easily, and only ores with a high sulphur content – about half of those used at Hafod – were suited to the new furnaces. Furthermore, as a bulky low-cost product, sulphuric acid could be sold only to local buyers, principally to tinplate manufacturers who used the acid for 'pickling' or cleaning the thin iron sheets before plating. Yet in spite of these limitations, the Vivians – at a cost of £60,000 – converted all their furnaces at Hafod and Taibach, using the acid in purpose-built alkali and superphosphate plants.[32]

The evidence that Gerstenhofer condensers reduced both the volume of smoke and emissions of the deadly sulphurous acid gas seemed clear and incontrovertible. For the first time there was hope, the *Cambrian* exclaimed excitedly, that 'men . . . will not think of Hafod as the blackness of darkness for ever', and that 'we may yet see our hillsides once again verdant, and our vallies rejoicing with a rich and beautiful foliage'.[33] Yet in spite of the promise of Gerstenhofer's invention only three of Swansea's eleven copper companies installed the condensers and neither the Swansea Board of Health nor central government was prepared to coerce the delinquents – the one from long habit and the other from genuine fear of obstructing an important industry. The right invention had come at the wrong time. The Welsh copper industry was no longer in the ascendant and government, anxious not to undermine its competitive position, refused to order the use of the condensers. After weighing the evidence provided by a number of Swansea coppermasters, including Hussey Vivian, the commissioners investigating injuries from noxious vapours, in 1878, decided that copper works could not be expected to meet the standards set by the Alkali Act. In place of compulsion, they suggested a system of inspection whereby inspectors working under the Alkali Act would recommend the most practicable means of preventing the escape of noxious gases.[34] Local government boards might be empowered to demand the adoption of the recommendations but in Swansea, of course, no board would ever lean heavily on a copper works. Copper once again had slipped the legal net.

8

The Cwmafan Disputes

꩜

Stac y Foel and the smelters at Cwmafan were also at the heart of the two final disputes in the long conflict over copper smoke. One was a heart-warming David and Goliath contest in the mould of the first Carmarthen trial, and the other a taut legal struggle between two evenly matched heavyweights. The legal battle, as a spokesman for the copper workers put it, matched the heiress of the richest commoner in England against the directors of one of the wealthiest and largest companies in the world. The heiress was the formidable Emily Charlotte Talbot, and the company the giant Rio Tinto.[1] To smelt its Spanish ores Rio Tinto, in 1884, bought and extended the disused plant of the English Copper Company in Cwmafan. Adjacent to the works, on the left bank of the Afan, were lands belonging to the Margam estate. In 1893, tenants of the estate farms complained of damage to crops and stock by copper smoke from the Cwmafan works. On clear and blustery days sea winds carried the smoke across Port Talbot and up the Neath valley, but in heavy, wet weather the smoke came down and settled on nearby farms and fields.

Margam estate was the property of Emily Charlotte Talbot, the second child and eldest daughter of Christopher Rice Mansel Talbot, Lord Lieutenant of Glamorgan, and owner of both the Margam estate and the Penrice estate in Gower. C. R. M. Talbot's presumptive heir was his son Theodore, Emily's senior by a year, but a hunting accident in 1876, which proved fatal, deprived him of his patrimony. When C. R. M. Talbot died in 1890 Emily inherited an estate valued at nearly £6 million, divided fairly evenly between railway investments and property. Rents alone, from 34,000 acres of land, brought in £44,000 annually. At fifty, Emily Charlotte Talbot was one of the richest women in Britain.[2]

She divided her time between the various Talbot houses: a London house in Cavendish Square, Penrice Castle (a Georgian mansion built by her grandfather) in Gower, and the more recently built Gothic Revival mansion at Margam Park. Margam, with its graceful orangery, flower gardens and rose-covered arched pergola, appears to have been her favourite residence.[3] She delighted in the gardens and when in London she arranged for daily deliveries by rail of flowers, fruit and vegetables. She was also much involved in the management of the Margam estate and concerned enough about the welfare of her farms and tenants that between 1890 and 1893 she spent more than £30,000 on repairs and new buildings.

On receiving complaints about damage by copper smoke, Miss Talbot took immediate action. She contacted Dr Vaelker of the Royal Agricultural College and sent samples of soil, hay and the viscera of sheep for laboratory testing. Sheep, in particular, had died in large numbers. The tests confirmed that both soil and hay were contaminated with sulphur and that the sheep had absorbed large quantities of copper. She also asked the Glamorgan County Council to reassess her estate. The council's assessor, whom Miss Talbot's agent found to be 'a perfectly independent man', concluded that copper smoke had affected the entire manor, reducing its value considerably.[4]

Lady Talbot's Injunction

To decide whether she had legal grounds for redress, Miss Talbot approached the chief inspector responsible for the enforcement of the Alkali Act. According to the terms of the 1881 Act, manufacturers were required to use the most practicable means available for reducing the emission of toxic and offensive gases. Copper works which used the gases to produce sulphuric acid were exempt from prosecution but Rio Tinto had not rebuilt the Gerstenhofer furnaces and condensers dismantled by its predecessor, the English Copper Company.[5] Under cover of the Act, and presumably on the advice of the chief inspector, who made at least a dozen visits to Margam, Miss Talbot served an injunction on Rio Tinto demanding that emissions of sulphurous acid gas at the Cwmafan works be reduced by half. Rio Tinto responded with the assertion that its ores, calcined in Spain, were relatively free of sulphur and that to meet the terms of the injuction it would have to move the entire smelting department to the ore fields.[6] The transfer would result in the immediate loss of between eighty and one hundred jobs and – by leaving only the roasting and refining processes at Cwmafan – might also lead to the eventual closure of the works. Removal of the smelting department, the company intimated darkly, would also halve the amount of coal needed from Oakwood colliery. The threat came at a time when the Welsh copper industry was clearly distressed. Metal sales in 1893 were only about a quarter of their peak (1850) values, and during the preceding three years the workforce at Rio Tinto had tumbled from approximately 1,500 to 700.

The workers' response to the injunction was swift and vehement. They saw themselves as helpless pawns in danger of being, as one of them put it, 'crushed between two stupendous interests'. The published correspondence generated by the dispute carried the dramatic rider: 'Cry for Bread Disregarded. Copper Industry of Wales in Danger of being driven out of the country to satisfy the Greed of Capitalists'. Miss Talbot and her tenants, the aggressors in the dispute, were immediately cast as villains. On a Saturday afternoon in August 1893 workers assembled quietly at Margam Park in the hope of reassurance from Miss Talbot but they were told, sensibly if somewhat imperiously, that until Rio Tinto responded to her demands she could have nothing to say to them.

Behind the workers stood the vicar of Cwmafan, the Reverend D. Bankes-Williams, and all the Nonconformist ministers of the town. Bankes-Williams chaired the public meetings and if Miss Talbot had been at all forthcoming he would have mediated between her and the workers. Both ministers and workers vilified the farmers. The Reverend John Evans, who farmed some land at Pwllygwlaw, thought that 'better cultivation and a little fresh seed' were all that were needed to improve crops and pastures. The Reverend G. Lloyd Evans, on the other hand, attributed their troubles not to ignorance, but to idleness: 'It was hard that an industrious community should suffer because of the laziness of a few farmers.' Thirteen or fourteen farms were said to be affected by the smoke. Most vituperative of all was Samuel James, a member of the Workmen's Committee: 'The farmers are at the root of all the evil. They are really spoilt children.'[7]

Some of the workers called for a torchlight procession through the town, but Bankes-Williams would have nothing to do with any action that hinted of aggression. In the end, the Workmen's Committee settled for a petition that gathered 3,200 signatures, virtually the entire population of Cwmafan over the age of sixteen. All the heat in the dispute was generated by the workers and the clergy. The two principals, protected by solicitors, kept their tempers and their counsel. Though reassured by Miss Talbot that her solicitors and Rio Tinto's were negotiating a settlement, the workers were given none of the details. Rio Tinto's spokesman, the general and technical manager James Osborne, was deliberately obfuscating while Miss Talbot, though straightforward, tended to be high-handed. She disclosed that her injunction had been served as retaliation against Rio Tinto's rejection of her initial claim for damages; and that in response to an appeal from the company for time to consider how it might modify its technical operations to meet the terms of the injunction, she agreed to delay its enforcement until fifteen months after January 1894. This would allow Rio Tinto twelve months in which to make changes, and Miss Talbot and her advisers three months in which to measure their effects.

After the injunction had been served, Rio Tinto declared its willingness to pay damages, and in her curt correspondence with the workers' committee Miss Talbot indicated that a tentative agreement had been reached, the details of which were being worked out by their respective solicitors. Because matters were under negotiation she saw no point in meeting another deputation of workers and steadfastly refused their request for an audience. She did, however, reassure them that she had no intention of forcing the removal of the smelting department to Spain, nor did she think that Rio Tinto had ever seriously contemplated such a move. In private the company, which was never in danger of having to move the smelting department, spoke only of expansion. One of the conditions of settlement demanded by Rio Tinto was the enlargement of the Port Talbot docks to accommodate ships of up to 2,500 tons.

Rio Tinto's role in the dispute was the tiresome one of injured inno- cent. Its ores, treated in Spain before shipment, were already 'the purest in use' with a sulphur content of only 10 to 20 per cent compared with 30 to 50 per cent of its predecessor, the English Copper Company. To work efficiently, Gerstenhofer furnaces needed ores with a high sulphur content, so that only by moving the smelting department to the ore fields could the company meet the terms of the injunction. Arrangements were being made to build new furnaces in Spain. It was unfortunate, manager James Osborne sighed resignedly, but Miss Talbot left them no choice; 'we are perfectly in her power'. In his meetings with the workmen and their clerical advisers, Osborne passed quickly over the subject of current negotiations for damages, pausing only to disclose the severity of Miss Talbot's initial request. She had insisted that Rio Tinto take over the damaged farms and pay the then current level of rent for the next thirty years. At the end of the rental the company would also pay twenty-eight times the amount of any depreciation in the value of the property. She also insisted that the company take coal from her collieries, pay certain import, export and way-leave duties, and send all traffic to Port Talbot over a railway laid down by her.[8]

Unlike Miss Talbot, Rio Tinto's spokesmen never admitted that the company was negotiating a settlement. By keeping the workers and the clergy agitated with veiled threats of a possible move to Spain, Rio Tinto brought pressure on Miss Talbot to withdraw the injunction and modify her demands. In the end she stooped a little so that the workers would not be conquered, withdrawing the injunction in exchange for damages of £1,400 followed by annual payments of £700.

Morrison and Rees versus Rio Tinto

In spite of the settlement with Miss Talbot, Rio Tinto's troubles in Cwmafan were far from over. Encouraged by Miss Talbot's success, several farmers made small claims for damages against the company. Among the claimants were William Rees, tenant of Fforchlas, a 573-acre mountain farm in the Creggan valley, and his landlord Hugh Morrison; the Creggan is one of the headwaters of the Afan. Rees claimed damages of £450 and Morrison of £200, even though in the pre-trial correspondence they maintained that the actual damages were about £1,000. Rio Tinto denied any liability for the alleged injuries, but in the interests of keeping the peace and avoiding costly litigation it responded with an initial offer of 10 guineas to each in settlement of all claims. On the advice of Professor Haacks, a veterinarian and land valuer, the offer to William Rees was subsequently raised to £75. Neighbouring farmers had accepted settlements of £30–£100. Both the initial and subsequent offers were rejected as 'ridiculous', Morrison countering with a demand of £125 and Rees of £250. Rio Tinto ignored both. Angered by the contrast between Rio Tinto's generosity with Miss Talbot and its niggardliness with – as Rio Tinto obviously saw them – 'poor ignorant farmers', Morrison and Rees decided to sue. The venue for the trial was the Glamorgan Summer Assizes at Swansea in 1895.

The action was easily the most important of the Assize, meriting, the *Cambria Daily Leader* reported, no fewer than three official shorthand writers and an 'array of legal talent': Abel Thomas and S. T. Evans for the plaintiffs, and J. C. Bigham and Clement Higgins for the defendants.[9] Bigham, a 'combative counsel', and Higgins were both prominent London QCs. The positions taken by the disputants were the now thoroughly familiar ones. Rees and Morrison sought damages for injuries to pasture, stock and land, whereas Rio Tinto, as heir to the English Copper Company in Cwmafan, claimed a prescriptive right to smelt copper in the valley. Not only was the company operating in a convenient place and in a proper manner, but it was doing so in a district where copper smelting had been sanctioned by custom and usage. Abel Thomas, leading counsel for Rees and Morrison, opened by enumerating the losses suffered by his clients. Eight years earlier the farm had supported 400 sheep, fifteen cattle and three horses. By 1895 the numbers had fallen to sixty sheep, four cattle and one horse, a fourfold loss in carrying power. A common pasture on Tonmawr mountain, which had once supported thousands of sheep, could sustain only hundreds at the time of the trial. The source of the mischief, averred Abel Thomas, was smoke from Stac y Foel that laid down a fine dust of copper over the entire district.

of the claims had not been made until Miss Talbot had obtained her injunction. The injunction had whetted the appetites of farmers who thought they had found, in Rio Tinto, a potential goldmine. It was a form of blackmail that Rees and Morrison had raised to intolerable levels. By refusing to accept reasonable terms, they had forced the company to make a stand. He ended with a little blackmail of his own. He warned the jury that if the claims of the plaintiffs were found it would set such a precedent that Rio Tinto would be forced to leave Cwmafan. He thought that there was no need to elaborate on the dire consequences of such a move for families in the district.

First to testify for Rio Tinto was Mr Dor, works manager at Cwmafan. He repeated the argument, used against Lady Talbot, that because the ores used at Cwmafan were calcined in Spain, condensing chambers would not have been practicable. He also pointed out that condensers reduced but did not eliminate emissions of sulphurous acid gas. The Cape Copper Works near the mouth of the Nedd had condensing chambers and an associated chemical plant but it still released sulphurous gases into the air. He knew of no practical method of condensing the gases from the Rio Tinto works. Dor conceded that copper smoke laden with sulphurous acid gas was most destructive of vegetation, and that nothing grew for three miles around the calciners at Rio Tinto in Spain. But, he pointed out, Rio Tinto's loss was Cwmafan's gain; the already calcined ores used at Cwmafan were relatively harmless. His own garden on the side of the mountain about 900 yards below the stack was unaffected by the smoke.

John Allen, a chemist employed by the United Alkali Company, affirmed that the quantities of sulphurous gases given off by the Cwmafan furnaces were so small that it was neither necessary nor possible to condense them. He conceded that smoke from Stac y Foel killed vegetation immediately around the base of the stack but maintained that within half a mile of the stack the smoke was so weakened that grasses and bracken were 'absolutely undamaged'. The black deposits on the stone walls he attributed chiefly to lichen which had withered and formed a black coating. But when Abel Thomas, the prosecuting counsel, produced a discoloured stone and asked him to taste a scraping of the deposit he was forced to admit that it contained copper. He was further embarrassed when Abel Thomas elicited the admission that, when examining the grasses, Allen had not conducted tests for the presence of arsenic and sulphur. His entire testimony rested, as Justice Lawrance was moved to remark, on the assumption that smoke more than half a mile from the stack was so diluted that it could not harm vegetation. Whether the assumption was right or not, his Lordship exclaimed, was another matter.

While John Allen was being re-examined by the defence, bunches of roses and trays of peas, parsley and gooseberries picked from a garden in the neighbourhood of the stack were passed around for inspection by the jury. The exhibits served to introduce the next witness, a professional gardener from Cwmafan. They were also the occasion for a little gallows humour. Justice Lawrance remarked that the jurors were lucky that the defence had produced fruit and vegetables, not a rotten sheep. John Morris, a gardener at Coedparc, spoke of the perfect health of his flowers and plants. Coedparc was a mile away from Stac y Foel as the crow flies, and although smoke often drifted over the park, Morris had never known it to interfere with the growth of plants.

As in each of the previous copper-smoke trials, witnesses were called to refute the evidence of the farmers who had appeared for the plaintiffs. Butchers from Cwmafan testified that animals raised on pastures exposed to the smoke were in no way inferior to animals raised elsewhere. Charles Linnaker, a land agent and valuer for the marquis of Cholmondeley, had examined the neighbourhood and found that at a mile and a quarter from the stack the vegetation was fresh and vigorous. Mr Miller, JP, member of the Brecon County Council and a sheep farmer and land agent, was struck by the brown colour of the grasses on the south and south-east sides of William Rees's farm. These so reminded him of his own farm that he returned to Brecon that same night to compare appearances. He found the same brown grasses on southern and eastern slopes where the soil was thin and rough, and concluded that in both cases the grasses suffered from poor soil and burning by the sun. He saw nothing in the Creggan valley that could be attributed to copper smoke but freely admitted, when cross-examined, that he had no experience of farming in copper-smelting districts. Ignorance, however, did not prevent him from offering gratuitous advice. He suggested that more fencing to control the movements of stock might cure the ills of the Creggan valley farm: the lower parts of the farm could be used for winter grazing and the mountain pastures for summer. On upland farms in the headwaters of the Afan, the seasonal movement of stock was as standard a practice as in Breconshire.

Professor Haacks, the veterinarian, examined seventeen sheep alleged to have died from copper smoke. Of the seventeen only seven had died from diseases that he was unable to identify, but he acknowledged that these unattributed deaths might be connected to copper smoke. Haacks disclosed that he had submitted a report of his findings to Rio Tinto but neither J. C. Bigham nor Judge Lawrance would grant Abel Thomas's request that the report be produced in court. Mr Portuse, the head chemist at the Cwmafan works, who had also examined several dead sheep, testified that he had found small traces of copper in a few spleens and kidneys. He found no arsenic. He had also found small traces of copper in the grasses, but again no arsenic.

The final witness of the exhaustive six-day trial was a fellow of the Chemical Society, Mr Davies, who declared that copper was dangerous to animals only if ingested in large amounts. He thought that small quantities of copper taken over a long period of time would be unlikely to poison sheep when much larger doses were given to them medicinally with beneficial results.

J. C. Bigham, counsel for Rio Tinto, ended as he had begun – with a two-hour speech. He combated 'with great vigour' the contention of the plaintiffs that the sheep had died from copper poisoning, or from anything other than ordinary diseases or ailments. He placed great store in the evidence of the Cwmafan butchers, who had bought perfectly healthy sheep within half a mile of Stac y Foel, and in the evidence of the Brecon farmer, Mr Miller, who had questioned the effectivness of farming practices in the upper reaches of the Afan valley. He also dealt in detail with the scientific evidence but in the end he relied more heavily on the testimony of gardeners in Cwmafan who had sworn that hedgerows, trees and gardens in the district were absolutely uninjured. On the basis of such evidence, he declared that the only reasonable conclusion a jury could reach was that the gases discharged from the stack were 'absolutely harmless' to vegetation.

No sooner had J. C. Bigham finished than Abel Thomas, counsel for the plaintiffs, was 'immediately upon his feet'. He dealt 'in minute detail' with the evidence of each witness called by the defendant and stressed the point that Rio Tinto's prior payment of damages to farmers in the Afan valley was tantamount to an admission of guilt. This being the case, the only question for the jury to decide was the amount of damages sustained. He ridiculed the assertion that Rio Tinto would be forced to move the works if the verdict went against the company and he urged the jurymen to rid themselves entirely of the idea.

In his summing-up, Justice Lawrance asked the jurors to address two main questions: first, whether the plaintiffs, Morrison and Rees, had suffered from smoke issuing from Rio Tinto's chimneys; second, whether the smoke over the Creggan valley was greater in volume and more harmful in 1895 than it had been twenty years earlier. To answer the first question, he issued the jurors clear directions. Morrison and Rees were not the only complainants and Rio Tinto's payments to Miss Talbot and to independent farms in the Afan valley were tantamount to an admission that smoke from Stac y Foel had injured crops and stock. The plaintiffs were clearly owed damages.

Unlike the jurors at most of the earlier trials, the Swansea jurors did not hurry their judgment. They deliberated from 4.30 p.m. until 10.00 p.m. and on their return they affirmed Rio Tinto's prescriptive right to smelt copper in the Afan valley. None of the jurors thought that the smoke over Creggan valley was greater in volume or more damaging than it had been twenty years earlier. But on the question of damages they were divided irreconcilably. The *Cambrian* reporter gave the count as eleven to one, presumably in favour of the plaintiffs given the nature of the judge's charge to the jury, but he did not elaborate. Without unanimity there could be no verdict. Mr Justice Lawrance had no choice but to declare a *remanet* and adjourn the trial. Goliath might have been a weakened giant but in a Swansea courtroom no David, even one as sturdy as William Rees, would ever injure him.

9

The Decline of the Kingdom

Although inconclusive, the Swansea trial in effect was a clear victory for Rio Tinto. Yet neither the company nor the industry as a whole was to savour it. By the end of the century, the prohibitive costs of shipping concentrates shifted the balance of advantages from the coalfields to the ore fields. Between 1890 and 1900 Britain's imports of manufactured copper rose from a little more than 5,000 tons to nearly 350,000 tons. Bowing to the economic pressure, in 1906 Rio Tinto did what it had threatened to do a decade earlier – it moved its smelting operation to Spain, closed the Cwmafan works and built a small refinery at Port Talbot docks. It was the last investment in copper smelting in the Swansea district. Unable to command supplies of cheap concentrates, the copper companies closed their doors; by 1921 every furnace in the Tawe valley was idle and every chimney cool and still. A few specialist works lingered in the region but the vitality of the industry had gone. Though the decline was precipitous its approach had been signalled as early as 1842 when Charles Lambert, using Welsh coal, began producing concentrates at his La Serena works. 'Coal out' may have reduced the costs of shipping ore home, but in the end it worked against Welsh smelters by encouraging smelting on the ore fields. When, ten years later, Lambert built the Port Tennant works to refine his 'Chili bars', Welsh coppermasters, who sensed the threat to the integrity of their industry, are said to have been incensed. In Port Tennant, Swansea had been reduced to a refining or finishing centre.[1]

While a patent threat to Welsh smelters, the reduction or concentration of the ore at or near the mines and ore fields was an extension of normal practices rather than a departure from them: to reduce freight charges, it had been the custom from the outset to 'pick' and 'dress' the ores before shipping. As the richer lodes in the producing countries became worked out, the costly and dangerous practice of sending heavy ores half-way around the world became more difficult to justify. Low-grade ores, as the encyclopaedist C. Tomlinson noted in 1852, 'will not pay for being brought to England'.[2]

There was, too, a natural tendency to go beyond concentration or reduction to full smelting. Chiefly due to the success of Lambert's reverberatory furnaces at La Serena, between 1842 and 1847 copper smelting in Chile and Peru increased fivefold. By the 1840s there were coal-using reverberatories in the United States, and by the 1850s the English and Australian Company (which operated the Spitty works, Loughor, 1852–6) had built smelters in New South Wales.[3] When the historian Grant Francis returned to Swansea after an absence of some months in 1869, he remarked gloomily that the Welsh copper industry was already in a state of 'change and decadence'. Although output would not decline until the end of the century, Chileans and Australians were exporting rough or bar copper at prices so threatening to Welsh smelters that some of these turned their attention to the manufacture of zinc.

As well as reducing costs of production, smelting abroad was a response to a surge in the demand for copper created by the growth of manufacturing and, toward the end of the nineteenth century, the needs of mass electrification. Of the common metals, copper has the highest rate of conductivity. To meet the demand for copper, smelters in the New World had been quick to take up new techniques. Americans, who by 1895 were smelting one half of the world's copper, adopted the methods of electrolytic refining invented by James Elkington at Pembrey in the late 1860s. By the 1880s they were also using Bessemer converters, designed for making steel but, after modifications by Pierre Manhes, also able to smelt copper.[4]

Compared with American smelters, Welsh coppermen were extremely conservative. They had perfected the reverberatory furnace, and because they found it well suited to smelting the pot-pourri of ores that came to south Wales from many parts of the world they saw no need for change. For *aficionados* of smelting, the painstaking Welsh process represented a pinnacle of refinement, but for modernists it was a tiresome anachronism; Americans found it too difficult to manage and too costly to operate. Irritating, too, for Americans was the secrecy that still surrounded smelting in Wales and western Europe as a whole. Professor James Douglas, a visitor around 1900, found it 'ridiculous'. People who, he wrote, 'contribute nothing to the information of the world or their co-workers in any art, are not those who are generally most progressive in their own practice'.[5] As late as 1920, when the Welsh industry was in its death throes, jobs in the refining departments of some of the works were restricted to members of particular families. Birmingham-born Cecil Lewis, a refiner at Hafod early in the century, is said to have been the first 'outsider' to be entrusted with the secrets of the final stages of smelting.[6]

A measure of Welsh conservatism, according to critics of Welsh methods and attitudes, was the slowness to adopt the cheaper and more efficient Bessemer methods of refining. These reduced both the overall fuel-to-ore ratio and the number of stages in smelting. Defenders of Welsh methods, on the other hand, retort that in a region where labour and fuel costs were only half of those in America there was no great incentive to make the change. There had, too, they argue, been such marked efficiencies in Welsh methods of smelting between 1860 and 1885 that Swansea-trained engineers were drawn overseas to supervise the building of smelters.

Craft secrecy that seems to have been carried well beyond reasonable limits irritated local as well as foreign observers. A contributor to the *Cambrian* in 1894 asserted that the practice of employing Germans and Belgians in Tawe valley zinc works was largely a response to the absence locally of men with technical and scientific training.[7] Government recognition of the limitations of purely pragmatic and craft approaches to training in Britain as a whole led to the Technical Instruction Act of 1891. Swansea's strongest advocate of instruction in both the applied sciences and foreign languages was Hussey Vivian, the first Welsh coppermaster to employ Bessemer methods. He led the movement to bring a University College to Swansea, against the rival claims of Cardiff, and when the decision went in favour of Cardiff he generously agreed to become the College's first treasurer. As treasurer and (briefly) vice-principal, he urged the establishment of a professorship of applied mechanics. The Swansea Technical School, founded in 1895, was largely the fruit of Hussey Vivian's efforts.

The end of smelting in south Wales left wastelands in all the copper works towns. In the valley of the lower Tawe, where the industry had been so heavily concentrated, the legacy was a landscape so broken and so inimical to plant life that the analogies resorted to most frequently in attempts to describe it were the surface of the moon or the battlegrounds of the First World War. Over the lower three miles of the Tawe had been strewn, as in some massive geological unconformity, more than seven million tons of industrial and urban waste. For W. J. Gruffydd, poet and scholar, Landore was 'the most distressing sight in Britain'.

Official concern over the cataclysmic state of the valley dates from early in the twentieth century. In 1912 George Bell, a visionary borough surveyor, proposed that the tips be levelled, industrial sites created and a new valley road and tramway built. In response to the Housing, Town Planning Act of 1909, which empowered local authorities to prepare town-planning schemes for suburban areas, he also proposed that one side of the valley be converted into a 'garden suburb'.[8] His model might well have been Letchworth, the first of Ebenezer Howard's garden cities. The Great War precluded any decision or action, but the dream of redevelopment persisted. Nothing was achieved, however, until the inauguration of the now-celebrated Lower Swansea Valley Project in the 1960s. Marshalled by a former Colonial Service officer and Swansea man (Kenneth Hilton) and a distinguished historian (Professor John Parry), botanists, geologists, geographers, sociologists and economists from the University College of Swansea mounted a combined attack upon the physical and social problems of the valley. They were supported financially by the Nuffield Foundation, the Swansea Corporation and the Welsh Office.[9]

The aim of the project, as defined by John Parry (then principal of the college and chairman of the main committee), was practical redevelopment. The lower valley and Kilvey Hill were to be made 'useful and presentable', not fashioned into a 'sylvan glade'. New housing, new industry and green open space would replace the detritus of centuries. The command centre for the project was Singleton Abbey, the Vivian family home and, after 1920, the nucleus of the University College of Swansea. From the outset the College, which Hussey Vivian had tried to bring to Swansea, aimed to provide the scientific and technical education that he and his father had been forced to seek abroad.

The immediate goal of the Valley Project was to prepare the site for development. At the time, Swansea happened to be the headquarters for a regiment of engineers of the Territorial Army, and for both these and Regular Army engineering units the ruined valley was an ideal training ground. Waste tips were levelled or removed, stacks and old buildings bulldozed or blown up, and ponds and marshes filled in. Meanwhile, college and government scientists analysed tip wastes and soils as a preliminary to treating them with lime, fertilizer, organic material and sewage sludge. For plants, the most toxic of all the wastes were metallic slags from copper and zinc works. On the treated surfaces botanists planted trees and grasses, supplementing these on-site trials with experiments on tip materials in the college greenhouses and gardens. In the very grounds where Sarah Vivian had nurtured delicate exotics from Sikkim, and created a garden that was regarded as a triumph of art, botanists and agronomists experimented with grass and tree species that might be resilient enough to grow on the treated waste tips of the Tawe. The irony, had he been alive to see it, would no doubt have appealed to Hussey Vivian.

As well as being reshaped and replanted, the old surface also acquired new roads, houses, factories, warehouses and shopping centres. Apart from some residual housing, the nineteenth-century landscape has been obliterated. It is tempting to regard the reconstruction of the valley as the culmination of a process begun by Tawe valley farmers and landowners in the 1820s and 1830s. But to do so would be to project a modern sensibility upon the past. Although many of the landowners and farmers lamented the loss of once-attractive countryside, the real issue was property. Farmers were concerned to protect crops, soils and stock, not the environment or amenity. As entrepreneurs, the coppermasters, for their part, were exerting their right to smelt copper in a place that gave them the greatest economic advantage. Geography and the economics and technology of the nineteenth century had contrived to locate an offensive industry in a farmed and settled district. Conflict was inevitable. John Vivian of Cornwall put his finger on the dilemma in a letter to his son, John Henry Vivian of Swansea, at the first rustle of a long robe in the Tawe valley: 'Copperworks there must be', [and where else can they be] but where the coals are: – and wherever coals and copper works are, there will be plenty of inhabitants.'[10]

As we have seen, copper works eventually moved to where the ores are – in remote mountain and desert locations, for the most part. Copper smoke today is no less destructive than it was a century and a half ago and foreign heaths downwind of the smelters are as blasted as Kilvey Hill ever was. If a reincarnated George Borrow were to visit Sudbury, Ontario, the wasteland of bare and blackened rock that extends east of the town would provoke sentiments just as strong as those that led to his well-known 'Pandemonium' passage, written after his walk along the coach road from Swansea to Neath Abbey in 1853. But downwind of Sudbury, or Flin Flon, Manitoba, there are no fields, farms, villages, ruined abbeys or gentlemen's estates. Travellers and environmentalists may deplore such moonscapes but in these remote regions one never hears the rustle of a black robe. Few briefs are held for unproductive and unattractive nature.

Notes

છુ

Notes and Sources to Chapter 1

1. In the eighteenth century Robert Morris could still describe copper-making as 'almost a secret art and mystery'. Swansea Univ. Coll., Morris MS, 'History of the Copper Concern' (1774), 5. For the mystical associations of copper smelting see Gordon Parr, *Man, Metals and Modern Magic* (Ames, IA, 1958), 26–7.

2. Mining, too, was touched by mysticism. The memorial tablet to Charles Roe, an eighteenth-century copper smelter, reads: 'By an intuitive kind of knowledge he acquired an intimate acquaintance with the mineral strata of the earth.' See W. H. Chaloner, 'Charles Roe of Macclesfield (1715–81): an eighteenth-century industrialist', *Trans. Lancs. and Cheshire Antiquarian Soc.*, 63 (1952–3), 52–86.

3. Henry Hamilton, *The English Brass and Copper Industries to 1800* (2nd edn., London, 1967), 2–4.

4. William Rees, *Industry before the Industrial Revolution* (Cardiff, *Brass and Copper Industries*, 1968), 25.

5. Hamilton, 7.

6. Copper Devt. Assoc., *Copper through the Ages* (Radlett, Herts., 1934), 27–8.

7. Ibid., p. 9.

8. Lionel Williams, 'A sixteenth-century example of regional interdependence and alien participation in the mining industry: the exploitation of Cornish copper and lead ores and copper smelting at Neath, 1583–1587', *Morgannwg*, 3 (1959), 3–20.

9. For the history of copper smelting in Neath see C. D. J. Trott's comprehensive essay 'Copper industry', in Elis Jenkins (ed.), *Neath and District, A Symposium* (Neath, 1974), 111–49. Also instructive is Trott's 'Historical geography of the Neath region up to the eve of the industrial revolution' (Univ. of Wales MA thesis, 1946). The Cornish/German origins of copper smelting in Neath are covered in G. Grant Francis, *The Development of Copper Smelting in the Swansea District of South Wales from the time of Elizabeth to the Present Day* (2nd edn., Swansea, 1881). Except where otherwise indicated, all quotations relating to copper smelting in Neath may be found in these works.

10. For coal mining in Neath see C. D. J. Trott, 'Coalmining in the Borough of Neath', *Morgannwg*, 13 (1969), 47–74; and D. Rhys Phillips, *The History of the Vale of Neath* (Neath, 1925), 230–9.

11. George Eaton, *A History of Neath* (Swansea, 1987), 65–7.

12. M. B. Donald, *Elizabethan Copper* (London, 1955), 290.

13. For details of sixteenth-century smelting techniques see Donald, *Elizabethan Copper*, 184–212; and Rees, *Industry*, 157–71.

14. There are graphic descriptions of the 'humours' in copper smoke in Grant Francis, *Development*, 31–4.
15. George Eaton, *The Mackworths of the Gnoll* (Neath, 1990), 15.
16. Quoted in Francis Klingender, *Art and the Industrial Revolution* (London, 1972), 17. Klingender also pointed out that Yalden's praise might not have been wholly disinterested. At the time Sir Humphrey was facing charges of fraud in the House of Commons and Yalden's poem could have been part of a Tory campaign to exonerate him. The House of Commons voted Mackworth guilty of both fraud and violations of the Company's charter but he was saved by the fall of the Whig ministry.
17. For working conditions in the mines and Mackworth's efforts to recruit miners see Rhys Phillips, *History of Vale of Neath*, 233–7; Trott, 'Historical geography', 35–6; and Grant Francis, *Development*, 84–9.
18. Rhys Phillips, *History of Vale of Neath*, 236.
19. Moelwyn I. Williams, 'Economic and social history of Glamorgan 1660–1760', *Glamorgan County History*, 4 (Cardiff, 1980), 311–74.
20. Ibid., pp. 137–8.
21. Quoted in Trott, 'Copper industry', 139.
22. Grant Francis, *Development*, 77.
23. Revd Richard Warner, *A Second Walk through Wales* (London, 1799), 98–9.
24. R.O. Roberts, 'Penclawdd brass and copper works: a link with the slave trade', *Gower Journal*, 14 (1961), 35–41.
25. Daniel Defoe, *A Tour through the Whole Island of Britain* (London, 1745). Quoted in J. R. Ross, *Letters from Swansea* (Llandybïe, 1969), 31.
26. H. P. Wyndham, *A Gentleman's Tour through . . . Wales in the Months of June and July 1774* (London, 1775), 43–4.
27. R. O. Roberts, 'The smelting of non-ferrous metals since 1750', *Glamorgan County History*, 5 (Cardiff, 1980), 47–95.
28. For the geology and landforms of the lower Tawe valley see H. W. E. Davies, 'The development of the industrial landscape of south Wales during the 19th and 20th centuries' (Univ. of London M.Sc. thesis, 1955), 243–5.
29. 'History of the Copper Concern', 4.
30. Ibid., p. 147. Landowners in coal-rich districts quickly realized the potential of the market presented by the copper works. About 1760 the Mansell family, landowners in the lower Tawe, agreed to pay £600 toward the costs of constructing the Middle Bank works. 'Early copper works', *Lower Swansea Valley Factsheet 5* (Swansea, n.d.), 26.
31. Although the need for a reliable supply of coal at an economic price was critical, the decisive factor prompting the move, according to F. G. Cowley, was the inadequacy of the water supply at the old site. The production of sheet or plate copper required water-powered battery or rolling mills. F. G. Cowley, 'The Forest copper works and its site', *South West Wales Industrial Archaeology Soc. Bull.*, 31 (1952), 5–8.
32. Tom Ridd, 'Gabriel Powell: the uncrowned king of Swansea', *Glamorgan Historian*, 5 (1969), 153–60.
33. Grant Francis, *Development*, 98.
34. Ibid.

35. For Swansea's development as a resort see David Boorman, *The Brighton of Wales: Swansea as a Fashionable Seaside Resort 1780–1830* (Swansea, 1986).

36. William Cowper, 'Retirement', *Poetical Works of William Cowper* (London, 1874), 157.

37. Quoted in Boorman, *Brighton of Wales*, 90.

38. Quoted ibid., p. 92.

39. Gareth Rees, 'Copper sheathing: an example of technological diffusion in the English merchant fleet', *Journal of Transport History*, 1 (1971–2), 85–94; and J. R. Harris, 'Copper and shipping in the eighteenth century', *Economic History Review*, 29 (1966), 550–68.

40. 'The rise and fall of the copper industry', *Lower Swansea Valley Factsheet 7* (Swansea, n.d.), 22.

41. For details of investment in the copper industry see Roberts, 'Smelting', 57–9; and Paul Reynolds, 'Industrial development', in Glanmor Williams (ed.), *Swansea: An Illustrated History* (Swansea, 1990), 32–6.

42. W. O. Alexander, 'A brief review of the development of the copper, zinc and brass industries of Great Britain from A.D. 1500 to 1900', *Murex Review*, 1/15 (1955), 389–425.

43. R. O. Roberts, 'The White Rock copper and brass works, near Swansea, 1736–1806', *Glamorgan Historian*, 12 (1976), 136–51.

44. For the life and works of Thomas Williams see J. R. Harris, *Copper King* (Toronto, 1964).

45. Stephen J. Lavender, *New Land for Old* (Bristol, 1981), 12.

46. *Cambrian* (15 June 1822).

Notes and Sources to Chapter 2

1. Edward Donovan, *Descriptive Excursions through South Wales and Monmouthshire in the year 1804*, vol. 2 (London, 1805), 43–4.

2. Ibid., p. 44.

3. Luis Galdamez, *A History of Chile* (New York, 1941), 272–3.

4. Martin Phillips *The Copper Industry in the Port Talbot District* (Neath, 1935), 44–5.

5. Hopkin Morgan, 'The trade of Llanelly', *Carmarthenshire Local History*, 2 (1962), 32–54; and Llanelli Public Library, LC 672, 'Notes on the History of the Nevill Family', MS (n.d.).

6. M. V. Symons, *Coal Mining in the Llanelli Area* (Llanelli, 1978), 244–9, 286–8.

7. Ibid., p. 249.

8. For the agitation occasioned by early proposals for harbour development see W. H. Jones, *The Port of Swansea* (Carmarthen, 1922), 54–64; and Tom Ridd, 'Gabriel Powell', *Glamorgan Historian*, 5 (1969), 152–60.

9. *Opinions on a Floating Harbour at Swansea* (Swansea, 1831), 6–7.

10. Ridd, 'Gabriel Powell', 158.

11. The cartoon is reproduced in Jones, *Port of Swansea*, 61.

12. Ibid., pp. 65–103.

13. David Boorman, 'The port and its worldwide trade', in Glanmor Williams (ed.),

Swansea: An Illustrated History (Swansea, 1990), 57–84.

14. Robin Craig, 'The copper ore trade', in David Alexander and Rosemary Omner (eds.), *Volumes not Values: Canadian Sailing Ships and World Trade* (St John's, 1979), 277–96. See also *'Copper Ore Barques', Maritime and Industrial Museum Factsheet* (Swansea, n.d.).

15. Of the 114 new vessels registered in the port of Swansea between 1870 and 1874 ninety-one were built in eastern Canada. See Robert Craig, 'The Lanelly Iron and Shipping Company, *Nat. Lib. Wales Journal*, 10 (1957–8), 265–80.

16. William Richards was one of the Island's most successful entrepreneurs, not only building ships but conducting a far-flung mercantile business. With the decline of sail he turned to steam, becoming a director and major stockholder of the Charlottetown Steam Navigation Co. In 1870 he was elected by acclamation to the Prince Edward Island Legislature. PEI Public Archives and Records Office, HF 79.123, 'Notes on the Richards family', MS.

17. On 24 May 1874, the newly built barque *May*, commanded by Captain Williams, sailed from Port Hill (near New Bideford) for Swansea with a cargo of 34 tons of birch timber, 7,200 feet of deals, 2,350 boards and 18,638 bushels of oats. *Patriot* (28 November 1874).

18. Harold Davis, *An International Community on the St. Croix* (Bangor, 1950), 163; and Jones, *Port of Swansea*, 291.

19. Basil Greenhill and Ann Giffard, *Westcountrymen in Prince Edward's Isle* (Newton Abbot and Toronto, 1967), 164–5; and N. J. de Jong and M. E. Moore, *Shipbuilding on Prince Edward Island* (Ottawa, 1994), 362–3.

20. *Islander* (19 July 1867, 19 August 1870).

21. Harry Green, 'The Neath Abbey Iron Co.', *Trans. Neath Antiq. Soc.* (1980–1), 94–139; and Jones, *Port of Swansea*, 82.

22. David Turnbull, *Cuba* (London, 1840), 8–15.

23. The first Chilean ores (oxides and carbonates) came from an enriched surface blanket; the deeper ores (sulphides) contained less metal and more sulphur. When mining began the ores were so rich that the Chileans, who were ignorant of the technique of slow roasting before smelting, rejected copper pyrites, the most common ore in Cornwall.

24. WGAS, Vivian Coll., D/DGV 16. Charles Madge, Report of his visit to Chili and Peru, 1881.

25. Charles Darwin, *The Voyage of the Beagle* (London, 1831), 241, 309.

26. Charles Lambert was a French mining engineeer who after working for a mining company in Chile built smelters at Coquimbo and La Serena. He came to Swansea about 1840 where he built the Port Tennant copper works. WGAS, FAC 58/1, 'Account of the Bath family', MS.

27. Vivian Webber, *Journal of a Voyage round Cape Horn* (Swansea, 1859), 82–93.

28. Darwin, *Voyage*, 313.

29. R. Nelson Boyd, *Chili* (London, 1881), 156–9, 169–75; and G. F. Scott Elliot, *Chile* (London, 1907), 257.

30. W. H. S. Jones, *The Cape Horn Breed* (New York, 1956), 133–6.

31. Darwin, *Voyage*, 320–1.

32. WGAS, Vivian Coll., Madge, *Report*, 19.

33. *Swansea Cape Horners Remember* (Swansea, n.d.).

34. For a colourful account of shipboard conditions at the end of the nineteenth century see George E. Long, 'Conversations with Richard Sullivan', *South Wales Evening Post* (19, 21, 22 November 1956).

35. WGAS, Log of the *Cornwall* on a voyage from Swansea to South America, 1867–8.

36. WGAS, Log of the *Caldera* on a voyage from Swansea to South America, 1872.

37. Aled Eames, *The Twilight of Welsh Sail* (Cardiff, 1984), 47–55.

38. *Cambrian* (1875). 'Rogue' whales were sometimes whales whose mates had been killed by whalers. At the time the *Minstrel King* was off the coast of Brazil in waters frequented by whaling vessels from New England.

39. *Swansea Cape Horners Remember*, 13.

40. Jones, *Port of Swansea*, 290.

41. Joseph Conrad, *Mirror of the Sea* (1912; London, 1968), 12–13.

42. Jones, *Cape Horn Breed*, 131–2.

43. WGAS, Log of the *Herradura* on a voyage from Swansea to South America, 1872–3.

44. WGAS, Log of the *Caldera*, 1872.

45. In 1835, for example, R. J. Nevill agreed to pay Joseph Vivian of Camborne, a mine agent, 5 shillings per ton for every ton that exceeded the contracted amount of 1,200 tons. NLW, Nevill Records, 126. Agreement between Joseph Vivian of Camborne, miners' agent, and Richard Janion Nevill, 20 June 1835.

46. In the 1864 incident Samuel Dawkin, a Swansea shipkeeper aboard the *Mangosteen*, a barque from Cuba known to have had fever aboard during the voyage, was suddenly taken ill. He died on the third day showing all the symptoms of yellow fever. George Buchananan, *Report . . . on the Outbreak of Yellow Fever at Swansea*, appendix no. 16 to the eighth report of the Medical officer to the Privy Council with appendix, 1865 (London, 1866), 443.

47. For two fine recent accounts of the Swansea yellow fever epidemic see C. E. Gordon Smith and M. E. Gibson, 'Yellow fever in south Wales, 1865', *Medical History*, 30 (1986), 322–40; and William Coleman, *Yellow Fever in the North* (Madison, WI, 1987), 139–69.

48. A contemporary newspaper article, reprinted in the *Cambrian*, pointed to the stagnant parts of the 'great aerial ocean' as the source of epidemic atmospheres. Its author attributed to them not only epidemic diseases but certain anti-social racial or cultural characteristics. Among them were the supposed murderousness of the Maoris, the kleptomania of the Basutos and the aggression of the Fenians. *Cambrian* (6 October 1865).

49. Buchanan, *Yellow Fever*, 452.

50. For the aetiology of the disease and the circumstances that made possible the Swansea epidemic see Smith and Gibson, 'Yellow Fever', 329–35.

51. *Swansea Cape Horners Remember*, 44.

52. N. L. Thomas, *Swansea's Districts and Villages* vol. 2 (Swansea, 1969), 321.

53. 'Manufacture of copper', *South Wales Athenaeum* (1848), 20–1.

54. Richard Chadwick, 'Trading in ores 1600–1900', *Tamar Journal*, 5 (1983), 18–29.

55. John Percy, *Metallurgy* (London, 1861), 302–4.

56. *Morning Chronicle* (8 June 1850).

57. *Mining Journal* (27 November 1852).
58. NLW, Vivian Papers, 15116A. William Morgan, 'Notes from the Hafod copper works, 1873–1902'.
59. 'Pyrites', *The Copper Trade in Swansea, 1860–1914* (Edinburgh, n. d.), 8.

Notes and Sources to Chapter 3

1. Edward Donovan, *Descriptive Excursions through South Wales and Monmouthshire*, vol. 2 (London, 1805), 43.
2. Quoted in N. L. Thomas, *Swansea's Districts and Villages*, vol. 1 (Swansea, 1969), 105.
3. Martin Phillips, *The Copper Industry in the Port Talbot District* (Neath, 1935), 16.
4. J. T. Barber, *A Tour throughout South Wales and Monmouthshire* (London, 1803), 24.
5. Quoted in David Boorman, *The Brighton of Wales* (Swansea, 1986), 9.
6. James Rogers, *A Sketch of the Cholera Epidemic at Ystalyfera in the Autumn of 1866* (Swansea, 1867), 6–7.
7. J. M. Davies, 'The Morris family and Swansea', *Gower Journal*, 5 (1952). The observation on strike-breaking is made in Davies's MA thesis, 'The growth of settlement in the Swansea valley' (Univ. of Wales, 1940), 35. Robert Morris, founder of the Forest works, distrusted miners: 'First get honest miners, if there are such to be had ... I never knew an honest miner out of his own Country, and they are very scarce in their own.' Swansea Univ. Coll., Morris MS, 'History of the Copper Concern' (1774), 147.
8. Walter Davies, *General View of Agriculture and Domestic Economy of South Wales*, vol. 1 (London, 1815), 134–5. The Castle itself was finished before August 1773. See Bernard Morris, 'More evidence for the date of Morris Castle', *South West Wales Industrial Archaeology Soc. Bull.*, 62 (November 1994), 4–5.
9. An advertisement in 1811 for the sale or lease of the block cited twenty-four tenements.
10. Stephen Hughes and Paul Reynolds, *A Guide to the Industrial Archaeology of the Swansea Region* (2nd edn., Swansea, 1989), 49.
11. Quoted in J. E. Ross, *Letters from Swansea* (Llandybïe, 1969), 47.
12. G. J. Evans, 'Morriston: the growth and development of an industrial community' (Univ. of Wales BA thesis, 1964). See also 'The Morris family', *Lower Swansea Valley Factsheet 10* (Swansea, n.d.), 30–40.
13. Jeff Childs, 'The growth of the Morris estate in the parish of Llangyfelach 1740–1850', *Gower Journal*, 42 (1991), 50–67.
14. Iolo Morganwg's comments were made in his *Agricultural observations Made in a Journey thro some Parts of Glamorgan and Carmarthenshire in June 1796*. They are quoted in Childs, 'Growth of Morris estate', 56.
15. George T. Clark, *Report to the General Board of Health on a Preliminary Inquiry into the Sewage, Drainage, and Supply of Water, and the Sanitary Conditions of the Inhabitants of the Town and Borough of Swansea* (London, 1849).

16. Muriel Chamberlain, 'The Grenfells of Kilvey', *Glamorgan Historian*, 9 (1973), 123–42.

17. W. R. Lambert, 'Swansea and its copperworks', *Glamorgan Historian* 5 (1969), 206–12.

18. Clark, *Report*, 16–17.

19. Thomas Williams, *Report on the Copper Smoke and its Influence on the Public Health and the Industrial Diseases of Coppermen* (Swansea, 1854), 5.

20. Phillips, *The Copper Industry*, 54.

21. *Mining Journal* (27 March 1852).

22. Graham Hughes, *In the Valley Long Ago* (New York, 1985), 22–3.

23. A. Leslie Evans, *The Story of Taibach and District* (Port Talbot, 1963), 134.

24. R. R. Toomey, *Vivian and Sons, 1809–1924* (New York and London, 1985), 153.

25. Leslie Wynne Evans, 'Copper-works schools in the nineteenth-century', *NLW Journal*, 9/1 (1959), 1–22.

26. Evans, *The Story of Taibach*, 123.

27. NLW, Vivian Papers, L46, 'A brief history of the Hafod copperworks school, 1846–1905'.

28. *Reports of the Commissioners of Inquiry into the State of Education in Wales*, vol. 1 (London, 1847), 330.

29. *Cambrian* (4 September 1863).

30. Chamberlain, 134–6, and 'The Grenfells', *Lower Swansea Valley Factsheet 9* (Swansea, n.d.), 20.

31. Evans, *The Story of Taibach*, 60.

32. R. W. Jones, 'On the employment of children and young persons in the copper-works at Swansea and Llanelly', *Reports to the Commissioners on the Employment of Children* (London, 1842), 679–90.

33. Ibid., pp. 680–1.

34. Tom Ridd, 'Swansea's barrow boys and girls', *Gower Journal*, 17 (1967), 51–3.

35. Until the middle of the century beer was not only a far safer drink than most untreated water but it was also thought to promote strength and stamina. Many converts to teetotalism in the 1830s and 1840s expressed surprise that abstention had not weakened them.

36. *Mining Journal* (5 September 1840). R. H. Vivian writing as 'Y.Z'.

37. R. W. Jones, 'Employment of Children', 681.

38. Barber, *Tour*, 103.

39. R. O. Roberts, 'The smelting of non-ferrous metals since 1750', *Glamorgan County History*, 5 (1980), 62.

40. Lambert, 'Swansea', 208.

41. *Cambrian* (27 April 1849).

42. NLW, Vivian Papers, 15116A. William Morgan, 'Notes from the Hafod copper works, 1833–1904'.

43. R. O. Roberts, 'The development and decline of copper and other non-ferrous metal industries in south Wales', *Trans. Hon. Soc. Cymmrodorion* (1955), 78–115.

44. Toomey, *Vivian and Sons*, 148.

45. Prys Morgan, 'The Port Talbot district and the Blue Books of 1847', *Trans. Port*

Talbot and District Hist. Soc., 3/3 (1984), 84–97.

46. WGAS, Vivian Coll., D34/1/2. Agreement between William Howell of Swansea and John Henry Vivian of the Hafod Works, 1811.

47. Toomey, *Vivan and Sons*, 158.

48. T. Neville George, *A Social and Economic Survey of Swansea* (Cardiff, 1939), 26–7.

49. Grant Francis, *The Development of Copper Smelting in the Swansea District* (2nd edn., Swansea, 1881), 21.

50. Donovan, *Descriptive Excursions*, 54.

51. James Baker, *A Picturesque Guide to the Local Beauties of Wales*, vol. 1 (London, 1791), 123.

52. G. R. Lippett, 'The Morris family of Swansea' (Swansea Univ. Coll. Diploma in Local History, 1991), 46.

53. John Johnson designed both Clasemont and the Gnoll House at Neath. Thomas Lloyd, 'The architects of Regency Swansea', *Gower Journal*, 41 (1990), 56–69.

54. For the development of the Singleton estate see Ralph A. Griffiths, *Singleton Abbey and the Vivians of Swansea* (Llandysul, 1988); Bernard Morris, *The Houses of Singleton* (Swansea, 1995); and Averil Stewart, *Family Tapestry* (London, 1961), 115–26.

55. Ralph A. Griffiths, *Clyne Castle, Swansea* (Swansea, 1977).

Notes and Sources to Chapter 4

1. The first legal challenge to the power of the copper smelters occurred in England. To eliminate the costs of shipping ore inland to Macclesfield, in January 1768 the Macclesfield Copper Co. built a smelter on the Mersey below Liverpool. Complaints about smells and injuries to health and herbage began in September of that year and continued unabated. In 1770 the Liverpool Corporation, which called thirty witnesses to testify to the nuisance, successfully indicted the Company. The Company was ordered to move the calcining part of its operation immediately, and the entire works within two years. The new site was a mile from the old, on the south side of Liverpool. W. H. Chaloner, 'Charles Roe of Macclesfield (1715–81): an eighteenth-century industrialist', *Trans. Lancs. and Cheshire Antiq. Soc.*, 63 (1952–3), 52–86.

2. Quoted in N. L. Thomas, *Swansea's Districts and Villages*, vol. 2 (Swansea, 1969), 102.

3. *Cambrian* (19 January 1822).

4. Swansea Univ. Coll. Yorkshire Imperial Metals MS, 'Brief for the defendants John Henry Vivian and Sir Richard Hussey Vivian' (1833), 11.

5. NLW, Vivian Papers, A167. Letter from Arthur Jones to J. H. Vivian, May 1822. Jones was clearly incensed by the allegations of threats to animal life. In a letter expressing his outrage, appended to a bill sent to John Henry Vivian, the word animal is underlined.

6. *Cambrian* (13 May 1820).

7. NLW, Vivian Papers, A780–95. Letter from John Vivian to J. H. Vivian, 16 June 1820.

8. Ibid.

9. NLW, Vivian Papers, A782. Letter from John Vivian to J. H. Vivian, 27 January 1822.

10. John Vivian thought that copper works should be 'a fair object of legislation protection' against malevolent proceedings at law. NLW, Vivian Papers, A781. Letter from John Vivian to J. H. Vivian, 26 January 1822.

11. Griffiths, *Singleton Abbey and the Vivians*, 32.

12. *Cambrian* (19 January 1822).

13. *Proceedings of the Subscribers to the Fund for Obviating the Inconvenience Arising from Copper Smoke* (Swansea, 1822).

14. E. D. Peters, *The Principles of Copper Smelting* (New York, 1907), 437.

15. NLW, Vivian Papers, 15113B. Memorandum Book of William Jones, 13 October 1834.

16. NLW, Vivian Papers, 15112C. Notebook kept by J. H. Vivian describing processes at the Penclawdd Works, 1811. According to instructions issued by William Morgan, works manager at Hafod, to suppliers on Margam estate, poles with a diameter of not less than 7 inches were to be 22 feet long and poles not less than 9 inches across were to be 36 feet long. All were to be of hardwood, not fir. See Business Notebook kept by A. P. Vivian, 1840–98. WGAS, Vivian Coll., D/DGV 1a.

17. NLW, Vivian Papers, A177. Letter to J. H. Vivian from L. W. Dillwyn, 4 November 1822.

18. Elis Jenkins, 'William Weston Young', *Glamorgan Historian*, 5 (1969), 78–97. Young's talents also extended to salvage. In 1806 he contracted to salvage a cargo of refined copper from the sloop *Anne*, sunk in the Bristol Channel. Young's share was to be 15 per cent of the value (at sale) of the copper after all expenses had been paid. WGAS, Weston Young MSS, D/DXhf19. Agreement to salvage copper between William Weston Young, Frederick Pigou and William Grenfell, 1806.

19. Only smoke from the calciners was treated, the intensity of heat required by the melting furnaces brooking no interference with the draught. The smoke from the latter was, in any case, mostly coal smoke.

20. *Cambrian* (15 May 1822).

21. WGAS, Vivian Coll., D/DXhf14, 'Plan to destroy copper smoke', post-1814.

22. In a letter to John Henry Vivian, Anthony Hill, the Merthyr ironmaster and one of the judges invited to assess the experiments, referred to a visit by Wollaston to Swansea. NLW, Vivian Papers, A178. Anthony Hill to J. H. Vivian, 14 December 1822. One of Wollaston's many achievements was to produce pure platinum from which he welded vessels for the concentration and storage of sulphuric acid. Wollaston liked to spend part of each year visiting works and factories.

23. See Dafydd Tomos, *Michael Faraday in Wales* (Denbigh, 1973), 152–6; and Frank A. J. L. James (ed.), *The Correspondence of Michael Faraday*, vol. 1 (Stevenage, 1991), 284–5.

24. NLW, Vivian Papers. H. Davy to J. H. Vivian, 10 December 1824. In return, Davy sent (by coach) a haunch of venison and a recently killed cock pheasant which he thought would arrive in the right condition.

25. *Report to the Subscribers to the Fund for Obviating the Inconvenience arising from Copper Smoke* (Swansea, 1822), 15–67.
26. Within a year, however, the copper industry would have reason to be grateful for Young's ingenuity. Drawing on his experience of making china, Young invented a heat-resistant silica brick that could be used to line smelting furnaces, now burning hotter because of the increased height of the stacks. With the backing of a Neath ironmonger, Young built a brickworks near a source of siliceous sand at the head of the Nedd Valley. The bricks, which could also be used in steel-making furnaces, were a great sucess but Young made virtually nothing from his invention. A bankrupt at the time of the building of the brick-works, he could not be a legal partner to the enterprise. See Jenkins 'William Weston Young', 91–2.
27. The works was never built, its Cornish backers opting in 1835 for an alternative site at the foot of Mynydd y Foel in Cwmafan.
28. *Report to Subscribers*, 64–5.

Notes and Sources to Chapter 5

1. *Cambrian* (30 March 1833). The issue also contains the initial letter to the proprietors, written by Meyrick on behalf of the farmers. It stresses the desire to avoid costly litigation and the threat to the general welfare of the district that a legal action might bring.
2. Swansea Univ. Coll. Yorkshire Imperial Metals MS, 'Brief for the defendants' (1833), 7.
3. *Cambrian* (30 March 1833).
4. 'Brief for the defendants', 8.
5. NLW, Vivian Papers, A1129b. Richard Hussey Vivian to John Henry Vivian, n.d.
6. *Dictionary of National Biography*, vol. 50 (London, 1897), 399–402, which quotes from Peter Scarlett's *Memoir of Lord Abinger* (1877).
7. Reports of the trial may be found in the *Cambrian* (8, 16 March 1833), and *The Welshman* (8 March 1833). There is also a summary of the trial in Thomas Williams, *Report on the Copper Smoke and its Influence on the Public Health and Industrial Diseases of Coppermen* (Swansea, 1854), 40–7. Williams dubbed the proceeding the 'Great Copper Trial'.
8. Thomas Williams, *Report on the Copper Smoke*, 4.
9. Ibid., p. 46.
10. Thomas Williams, *A Sketch of the Relations which Subsist between the Three Kingdoms of Nature: The Mineral, Vegetable, and Animal* (Swansea, 1844), 71.
11. A major platform for the defence was that the farmers, aware of the effects of copper smoke, had 'come to the nuisance'. 'Brief for the defendants', 18.
12. According to the brief for the defendants both Lewis Weston Dillwyn and Michael Faraday were to have testified to the efficacy of Hafod's showers and tall stacks. Yet there is no record of their appearance at the trial. Faraday, who in his correspondence referred to being subpoenaed to Carmarthen, visited the works in 1833 and declared that he was 'astonished' at the success of the plan.

He remarked that the Vivians had done all that possibly could be done to suppress the smoke and if they were indicted it would be utterly impossible to continue the copper trade anywhere in Britain. 'Brief for the defendants', 63–4.

13. Mansell Phillips was also named as a witness for the Vivians but he, too, is not mentioned in the reports of the trial. He was to have testified that a farm near Hafod, presumably Penllwyn Robert, acquired in 1827 had doubled in value subsequently. 'Brief for the defendants', 36–8.

14. *Cambrian* (16 March 1833).

15. Swansea Univ. Coll., Grenfell MS, 'Brief for the defendants Pascoe Grenfell Esq. and Pascoe Grenfell the Younger Esq.' (1834), 15–18.

16. For a report of the trial see the *Cambrian* (9 August 1834).

17. 'Brief for the defendants' (1834), 21.

Notes and Sources to Chapter 6

1. 'King Copper and King Coal', *Cambrian* (21 December 1860).

2. John Charles Collins, MD, *A Sketch of the Medical Topography of Swansea* (Swansea, 1815), 7–8.

3. *Cambrian* (23 March 1822).

4. For a lively rebuke of Swansea's physicians see Paul Reynolds, 'Industrial health in nineteenth century Swansea', *South West Wales Industrial Archaeology Soc. Bull.*, 43 (1986), 3–5.

5. W. M. Frazer, *A History of English Public Health* (London, Balliere, 1950), 45–8.

6. *Proceedings of the Swansea Literary and Philosophical Institution* (1838), 31.

7. J. W. G. Gutch, 'On the medical topography, statistics, climatology, and natural history of Swansea, Glamorganshire', *Trans. Provincial and Medical Surgical Assoc.*, 7 (1839), 249–82.

8. Sir Henry de la Beche, *Report on the State of Bristol and other Large Towns* (London, 1845), 67–70.

9. Ibid., p. 67.

10. PRO, Home Office Papers, MH 13/178. L. W. Dillwyn to General Board of Health, 11 November 1848, reporting the decision taken at a recent ratepayers' meeting. As a community, Swansea had been markedly indifferent to the issue of public health. Attendances at meetings of the local sanitary authority between 1836 and 1843 averaged seven members out of a possible twenty-five. Tom Ridd, 'Municipal government in Swansea in the nineteenth century' (Univ. of Wales MA thesis, 1955), 193.

11. George T. Clark, *Report to the General Board of Health on a Preliminary Inquiry into the Sewage, Drainage, and Supply of Water, and the Sanitary Conditions of the Inhabitants of the Town and Borough of Swansea* (London, 1849).

12. Ridd, 'Municipal government', 202–3. On the basis of Clark's report a town committee, in 1849, recommended that the Public Health Act be applied to Swansea. PRO, Home Office Papers, 13/178. Letter C. B. Mansfield, Town Clerk, to General Board of Health.

13. S. C. Gamwell, 'Some Swansea men who have attained eminence in science', *Trans. Swansea Scientific Soc.* (1892–3), 34–9.

14. Margaret Walker, 'The British association in Swansea in 1848', *Gower Journal*, 22 (1971), 14–19. See also Tomos, *Michael Faraday in Wales*, 167–9. The British association meeting was the occasion for Michael Faraday's third visit to Wales.

15. Peter H. Thomas, 'Medical men of Glamorgan: Thomas Williams of Swansea, 1818–1865', *Glamorgan Historian*, 10 (1973), 70–95.

16. The Linnean Society Fellowship was withdrawn in 1859.

17. Thomas Williams, *A Sketch of the Relations which Subsist between the Three Kingdoms of Nature* (Swansea, 1844), 66–9. Swansea's sewers were so badly planned and constructed that they backed up when the tides were high. Ordinarily this would have been alarming but in a coastal town, Williams was quick to point out, it was a 'favourable circumstance', the antiseptic qualities of salt water effectively countering any 'malarial influence'.

18. PRO, Home Office Papers, MH 13/178. Thomas Williams to president of the General Board of Health, 27 January 1854.

19. Thomas Williams, *Report on the Copper Smoke and its Influence on the Public Health and Industrial Diseases of Coppermen* (Swansea, 1854), vii.

20. Ibid., 84–93.

21. *Cambrian* (10 October 1854).

22. *Cambrian* (8 December 1854)

23. The poison wave theory was still current thirty years later. The meteorologist J. Glaisher attributed the 1854 cholera epidemic to a dense blue mist that, unlike ordinary mists, did not blow away. *Cambrian* (10 August 1866).

24. Thomas Williams, *Report on the Copper Smoke* (1854), 12–13.

25. Ibid., 12.

26. Ibid., 101.

27. Ibid., 100.

28. 'Copper a cure against cholera', *Cambrian* (6 October 1865).

29. Quoted in John Rowlands, *Copper Mountain* (Llangefni, 1966), 21. Faith in vitriolic fluids as prophylactics against cholera persisted until the late nineteenth century. Hussey Vivian asserted that there was no more effective shield against cholera than dilute suphuric acid distilled from the sulphurous gases in copper smoke. During outbreaks of cholera he insisted that his men take mild solutions, diluted and flavoured so as to taste like lemonade. *Testimony to the Noxious Vapours Commission* (1878), 450.

30. *Cambrian* (9 July 1852).

31. Ibid.

32. *Cambrian* (30 January 1852).

33. Ibid.

34. Gerald Fielder, 'Public health and hospital administration in Swansea and West Glamorgan since the end of the eighteenth century to 1914' (Univ. of Wales MA thesis, 1962), 95.

35. PRO, Home Office Papers, MH 13/178. J. D. Berrington to General Board of Health, 13 October 1855.

36. A letter from the chairman of the Highways Board to the General Board of

Health asking if the directives of the Nuisance Removal Act were mandatory brought no response. Swansea Highways Board to the General Board of Health, 30 October 1855. PRO, Home Office Papers, MH 13/178.

37. PRO, Home Office Papers, MH 13/178. A. D. Berrington to the General Board of Health, 10 December 1855. A. D. Berrington was the son of the complainant, J. D. Berrington, who was in England at the time of writing. The Berringtons' property, Woodlands, was sold to Graham Vivian in 1860.

38. *Cambrian* (17 June 1859). Copper smoke was so sensitive an issue in mid-nineteenth-century Swansea that in the 1st edition (1867) of his book on the copper industry the historian G. Grant Francis made only a brief reference to it even though, in a letter to the *Cambrian* late in 1865, he condemned the smoke as an 'admitted evil'. In response to subsequent criticism that he had not done justice to the subject of copper smoke, in the 2nd edition of the book (1881) the smoke question is treated in an appendix. See G. Grant Francis, *The Development of Copper Smelting in the Swansea District of South Wales* (2nd edn., Swansea, 1881), 151.

39. Swansea City Archives, J. R. Alban MS, 'The portreeves and mayors of Swansea' (1982).

40. Robert M. Gutchen, 'Local improvements and centralization in nineteenth-century England', *Historical Journal*, 4 (1961), 85–97.

41. Law Reports, The Public General Statutes, Towns Improvement Clauses Act, 10 & 11 Vict., 34.

42. *Cambrian* (15 July 1859).

43. *Cambrian* (24 June 1859). Even Thomas Williams suffered a change of heart. Though convinced that no particular disease could be ascribed to copper smoke, he allowed, when supporting Michael's position, that the smoke was more or less prejudicial to health. *Cambrian* (28 September 1859).

44. *Cambrian* (20 May 1859).

45. PRO, Home Office Papers, MH 13/178. William Jowett to Local Government Act Office, 15 February 1859. The works in question was the 'Old Forest' copper works built by Robert Morris.

46. PRO, Home Office Papers, MH 13/178. H. H. Vivian to Local Government Act Office, 25 January 1859.

47. PRO, Home Office Papers, MH 13/178. Letter from H. H. Vivian to William Jowett, 3 February 1859.

48. PRO, Home Office Papers, MH 13/178. William Jowett to H. H. Vivian, 5 February 1859.

49. PRO, Home Office Papers, MH 13/178. H. H. Vivian to William Jowett, 7 February 1859. Jowett's spirited stand is celebrated in a lecture by Ieuan Gwynedd Jones: 'Health, wealth and politics in Victorian Wales' (Ernest Hughes Memorial Lectures, Swansea Univ. Coll., 1978).

50. A. Leslie Evans, *The Story of Taibach and District* (Port Talbot, 1963), 71.

51. *Cambrian* (12 August 1859).

52. PRO, Home Office Papers, MH 13/178. C. B. Mansfield to Local Government Act Office, 25 July 1859.

53. PRO, Home Office Papers, MH 13/178. Tom Taylor to C. B. Mansfield, 26 July 1859. Inadequacies in the 108th section of the Act, which exposed copper

smelters to unfair prosecution, were the subject of Taylor's testimony to the 1862 select committee on noxious vapours. Minutes of Evidence, *Report of the Select Committee on Injury from Noxious Vapours* (London, 1862), 236–9.

54. PRO, Home Office Papers, MH 13/178. Hussey Vivian and Pascoe Grenfell to Local Government Act Office, n.d.

55. PRO, Home Office Papers, MH 13/178. Tom Taylor to Hussey Vivian, 2 August 1859. The metallurgist John Percy, when commenting on the distinction, suggested that colour associations might have been operative: smoke is black, vapour white. John Percy, *Metallurgy* (London, 1861), 339.

56. Minutes of Evidence, *Report of the Select Committee on Noxious Vapours* (1862), 600.

57. *Cambrian* (12 August 1859).

58. *Cambrian* (21 December 1860).

59. House of Lords, *Report of the Select Committee on Noxious Vapours* (London, 1862), 619, 625.

60. Percy, *Metallurgy*, 339. Percy's remarks echoed a sentiment voiced at the time of the first patent fuel trial. A reader of the *Cambrian* was puzzled by the inconsistency of nostrils that could recoil from the smell of pitch and tar yet respond to the fumes of arsenic and sulphur as though these were 'etherial essences' as bland and as soothing as the choicest productions of Atkinson and Houbigand. *Cambrian* (23 January 1852).

61. *Cambrian* (9 July 1852).

62. *Cambrian* (21 December 1860).

63. Gutchen, 'Local improvements', 91.

64. *The Times* (11 August, 1866).

65. PRO, Home Office Papers, MH 13/178. Colonel Evan Morgan to Secretary of State, 17 August 1867.

66. *Cambrian* (15 May 1868).

67. PRO, Home Office Papers, MH 13/178. R. Rawlinson to Tom Taylor, 27 August 1867.

68. PRO, Home Office Papers, MH 13/178. Colonel Evan Morgan to Secretary of State, 13 October 1868.

69. *Cambrian* (22 May 1868).

Notes and Sources to Chapter 7

1. W. H. Jones, *The Port of Swansea* (Carmarthen, 1922), 314; and *Cambrian* (23 January 1841).

2. Michael here is unfair. In the late 1840s the Grenfells spent several thousand pounds on experiments to convert sulphurous gases in the smoke into sulphuric acid. The experiments, which left the Grenfells 'no wiser at the end than at the beginning', were conducted by Dr Charles Schafheutl, a German professor. Pascoe Grenfell, Minutes of Evidence, *Report of the Royal Commission on Noxious Vapours* (London, 1878), 465. Michael also ignored efforts to consume smoke at the White Rock works, a lapse that brought an accusation of 'calumny'. *Cambrian* (19 December 1859).

3. J. Percy, *Metallurgy* (London, 1861), 340.

4. Thomas Williams, *A Sketch of the Relations which Subsist between the Three Kingdoms of Nature* (Swansea, 1844), 72. In spite of the success of their tall stack and shower chambers, the Nevills continued their attack on smoke. In 1846, the Llanelli Copper Co. bought the patent of an invention that used steam jets to condense and collect sulphurous gases and metallic particles. NLW, Nevill Records, 553. Agreement between William Chambers and the Llanelli Copper Co., 5 September 1846. In 1855 the Llanelli Co. also the bought the rights for the sole use of a reverberatory furnace designed to condense and collect volatile substances. NLW, Nevill Records, 823. Letters Patent, 13 January 1855.

5. Paul Reynolds, 'Blaen Pelena peat charcoal works', *South West Wales Industrial Archaeology Soc. Bull.*, 35 (1984), 4–5.

6. *Cambrian* (9 September 1870).

7. Annette Sparkes, 'Dugdale Houghton 1799–1876: reading between the lines' (Swansea University College Diploma in Local History, 1991), 18. The occasion was reported in the *Cambrian* (28 November 1856).

8. Percy, *Metallurgy*, 447–50. See also W. H. Michael's testimony in *Report of the Select Committee on Noxious Vapours* (London, 1862), 575–6, 862.

9. The trial, which excited national interest, was held at the Central Criminal Court, London, May 1856. Grove, one of three assistants for the defence, cross-examined the prosecution's scientific witnesses.

10. Colin Matheson, 'William Robert Grove: Glamorgan physicist and judge', *Glamorgan Historian*, 9 (1973), 96–103.

11. For reports of the trial see the *Cambrian* (6, 13 August 1858).

12. Herepath appeared for the defence.

13. *Report of the Select Committee on Noxious Vapours* (1862), 577–8.

14. Thomas Williams, *Report on the Copper Smoke and its Influence on the Public Health and Industrial Diseases of Coppermen* (Swansea, 1854), 42–3.

15. *Cambrian* (21 January 1859).

16. For reports of the trial see the *Cambrian* (27 July 1860); and the *Swansea and Glamorgan Herald* (25 July 1860).

17. Sparkes, 'Dugdale Houghton', 24.

18. *Cambrian* (29 May 1863).

19. *Cambrian* (15 May 1863).

20. Elis Jenkins, 'Rheola', *Trans. Neath Antiq. Soc.* (1978), 61–8; and 'Welsh country homes', *South Wales Daily News* (25 March 1911).

21. *The Times* (6 September 1865).

22. *The Times* (4 September 1865).

23. *Cambrian* (24 October 1865).

24. *Cambrian* (27 October 1865).

25. *Cambrian* (24 November 1865).

26. Letter from Hussey Vivian to Nash Vaughan, *Cambrian* (11 August 1865).

27. Quoted in G. Grant Francis, *The Development of Copper Smelting in the Swansea District of South Wales* (2nd edn., Swansea, 1881), 158–9.

28. The decision might well have been influenced by an injunction obtained against the St Helens Smelting Co., Lancs, the previous November. The owner of the 1,300-acre Bold Hall estate, near St Helens, succeeded in shutting down smelters

built, in 1861, within half a mile of the boundary of the estate. Following the award of damages from a common-law court in 1863 he took the issue to an equity court and obtained the injunction even though the St Helen's Co. had installed steam jets and lead condensing chambers in an attempt to eliminate gases from the smoke. 'Tipping v. the St Helen's Smelting Co.', *Cambrian* (24 November 1865, and 13 July 1866). In June 1866 the Oldbury, Glos., Local Board of Health also succeeeded in closing the recently erected works of the Staffordshire Copper Extracting Co. The action, in which more than 200 witnesses affirmed the threat to their health and comfort, was defended by W. R. Grove. *Cambrian* (6 July 1866).

29. Grant Francis, *Development*, 160.
30. Martin Phillips, *The Copper Industry in the Port Talbot District* (Neath, 1935), 43.
31. R. A. Smith, the first chief inspector appointed under the 1862 Alkali Act, estimated that about 30 per cent of the sulphurous gases were retained, roughly half of the amount claimed by Hussey Vivian. Minutes of Evidence, *Report of the Royal Commission on Noxious Vapours* (London, 1878). Before the same commission Pascoe Grenfell also testified that Gerstenhofer condensers were not a complete remedy, rather 'a mere scotching of the snake'. He declared that if he were required to build Gerstenhofer condensers he would close the works altogether.
33. *Cambrian* (22 September 1865).
33. *Cambrian* (11 August 1865).
34. Of the Swansea coppermasters only Hussey Vivian objected to a system of inspection. He considered Tawe valley lands in the vicinity of the works to be 'beyond cure' and, 'as a free Englishman', he would have found it intolerable to have inspectors running over his works. *Report of the Royal Commission on Noxious Vapours* (1878), 27.

Notes and Sources to Chapter 8

1. *Cwmavon Copper Works Smoke Dispute* (Swansea, 1894), 13. This *Evening Post* booklet is a comprehensive record of the dispute. It contains letters written by Miss Talbot, her agent William Knox, James Osborne the Technical Manager of Rio Tinto and spokesmen for the workers. Also included are reports of public meetings and transcripts of exchanges between representatives for the workers and the agents for Rio Tinto and the Margam estate.
2. John Vivian Hughes, 'Emily Charlotte Talbot', *Trans. Port Talbot Hist. Soc.*, 3/2 (1974), 85–95.
3. D. John Adams and Arthur Rees, *A Celebration of Margam Park and Gardens* (Port Talbot, 1989).
4. *Cwmavon Copper Works Smoke Dispute*, 32.
5. Alkali and Works Regulation Act, Law Reports, The Public General Statutes, 1881, 44 & 45 Vict., 29.
6. The move would not have pleased the farmers and landowners of Huelva province. In the 'smoke riots' of 1888 these protested violently against the open-

air calcination of the pyritic ores. Bowing to its traditional supporters, the Madrid government ruled that the calcination should cease on grounds that it was damaging to human health. But under pressure from Rio Tinto and the Madrid Academy of Medicine, which declared the smoke harmless to humans, the government suspended its ruling. Charles E. Harvey, *The Rio Tinto Company: An Economic History of a Leading International Mining Concern 1873–1954* (Penzance, 1981), 138–9; and Edmund Newell, 'Atmospheric pollution and the British copper industry, 1690–1620', *Technology and Culture*, 38 (1997), 655–89.

7. *Cwmavon Copper Works Smoke Dispute*, 32.
8. Ibid. p. 47.
9. For reports of the trial see *South Wales Daily Post* (28 June–4 July 1895), *Cambria Daily Leader* (28 June–4 July 1895) and *Cambrian* (5 July 1895).

Notes and Sources to Chapter 9

1. For details of the shift of smelting to the ore-producing countries see R. O. Roberts, 'The development and decline of copper and other non-ferrous metal industries in South Wales', *Trans. Hon. Soc. Cymmrodorion* (1955), 102–7; and Edmund Newell, 'Copperopolis: the rise and fall of the copper industry in the Swansea district, 1826–1921', *Business History*, 32 (1990), 75–97.
2. To offset transportation costs foreign ores had to have metal contents of at least 15–25 per cent.
3. Roberts, 'Development and decline', 103.
4. Leslie Aitchison, *A History of Metals*, vol. 2 (New York, 1960), 523.
5. Quoted in Roberts, 'Development and decline', 106.
6. Swansea City Archives, TH. 34, 'Cecil Lewis – copperman'.
7. *Cambrian* (7 February 1894).
8. John Barr, *Derelict Britain* (Harmondsworth, 1969), 88.
9. For details of the five-year study and proposals for restoration see K. J. Hilton, *The Lower Swansea Valley Project* (London, 1967). There is an excellent summary of the project in Barr, *Derelict Britain*, 79–156.
10. NLW, Vivian Papers, A740. Letter from John Vivian to J. H. Vivian, 28 May 1820.

Bibliography

MANUSCRIPT AND UNPUBLISHED SOURCES

Llanelli Public Library
Notes on the History of the Nevill Family, LC 672.

National Library of Wales
Nevill MSS
Vivian MSS

Public Record Office
Home Office Papers, MH 13/178

Prince Edward Island Public Archives and Records Office
Notes on the Early History of the Parish of Port Hill (Thomas R. Millman, 1941)
Notes on William Richards and the Richards Family, HF 79.123

Swansea City Archives
The Portreeves and Mayors of Swansea (J. R. Alban, 1982)
Cecil Lewis – copperman. Taped interview with Cecil Lewis, TH 34

University of Wales Swansea
Brief for the Defendants Pascoe Grenfell, 1832
Brief for the Defendants John Henry Vivian and Sir Richard Hussey Vivian, 1833,
    Yorkshire Imperial Metals MS
Lippett, G. R., 'The Morris family of Swansea' (Univ. Coll. Swansea Diploma in
    Local History, 1991)
Morris, Robert Jr., 'History of the copper concern, 1717–30'
Sparkes, Annette, 'Dugdale Houghton 1799–1876: reading between the lines' (Univ.
    Coll. Swansea Diploma in Local History, 1991)
Thomas, Janet, 'Swansea as a fashionable watering place 1787–1820' (Univ. Coll.
    Swansea BA thesis, 1983)

University of Wales
Davies, J. M., 'The growth of settlement in the Swansea Valley' (Univ. of Wales MA
    thesis, 1940)
Evans, G. J., 'Morriston: the growth and development of an industrial community'
    (Univ. of Wales BA thesis, 1964)
Fielder, Gerald, 'Public health and hospital administration in Swansea and West
    Glamorgan since the end of the eighteenth century' (Univ. of Wales MA thesis, 1962)
Ridd, Tom, 'Municipal government in Swansea in the nineteenth century' (Univ. of
    Wales MA thesis, 1955)
Trott, C. D. J., 'An historical geography of the Neath region up to the eve of the
    Industrial Revolution' (Univ. of Wales MA thesis, 1946)

BIBLIOGRAPHY

West Glamorgan Archives Service
An Account of the Bath and Lambert Families, FAC 58/1
Logs of the *Alpha*, 1866–7; *Caldera*, 1872–3; *Cornwall*, 1867–8; and *Herradura*, 1872–3
Vivian Collection
William Weston Young Collection

OFFICIAL PAPERS

Buchanan, Dr George, *Report . . . on the Outbreak of Yellow Fever at Swansea, Appendix no. 16 to the Eighth Report of the Medical Officer to the Privy Council with appendix, 1865* (London, HMSO, 1866)

Clark, George T., *Report to the General Board of Health on a Preliminary Inquiry into the sewage, drainage, and supply of water, and the sanitary conditions of the inhabitants of the town and borough of Swansea* (London, 1849)

de la Beche, Sir Henry, *Report on the State of Bristol and other Large Towns* (London, 1845)

Law Reports, The Public General statutes, Alkali and Works Regulation Act, 1881, 44 and 45 Vict.

Law Reports, The Public General Statutes, Towns Improvement Clauses Act, 1847, 10 and 11 Vict., 34

House of Lords, *Report from the Select Committee on Injury from Noxious Vapours* (London, 1862)

Report of the Royal Commission on Noxious Vapours (London, 1878, 1882)

Reports of the Commissioners of Inquiry into the State of Education in Wales (London, 1847)

Reports to the Commissioners on the Employment of Children (London, 1842)

PAMPHLETS AND REPORTS

Cwmavon Copper Works Smoke Dispute (Swansea, *South Wales Evening Post*, 1984)

Copper Through the Ages (Copper Development Association, Radlett, Hertfordshire, 1934)

Gabb, Gerald, Lower Swansea Valley Factsheets: 5, *Early Copper Works*; 6, *Later Copper Works*; 7, *The Rise and Fall of the Copper Industry*; 9, *The Grenfells*; 10, *The Morris Family* (Swansea, Swansea Museum, n.d.)

Proceedings of the Subscribers to the Fund for Obviating the Inconvenience Arising from Copper Smoke (London, 1822)

The New Swansea Guide (Swansea, 1823)

NEWSPAPERS

Cambria Daily Leader
Cambrian
Island Argus (Prince Edward Island)
Islander (Prince Edward Island)
Mining Journal

Jones, Ieuan Gwynedd, *Health, Wealth and Politics in Victorian Wales* (Univ. College of Swansea, Ernest Hughes Memorial Lectures, 1978).

Jones, W. H., *The Port of Swansea* (Carmarthen, 1922).

Jones, W. H., *The Cape Horn Breed* (New York, Criterion Books, 1956).

Jenkins, Elis, 'William Weston Young', *Glamorgan Historian*, 5 (1969), 78–97.

Jenkins, Elis (ed.), *Neath and District, A Symposium* (Neath, 1974).

Jenkins, Elis, 'Rheola', *Trans. Neath Antiquarian Society* (1978), 61–8.

Klingender, Francis, *Art and the Industrial Revolution* (London, Paladin, 1972).

Lambert, W. R., 'Swansea and its copperworks', *Glamorgan Historian*, 5 (1969), 206–12.

Lavender, Stephen J., *New Land for Old: The Environmental Renaissance of the Lower Swansea Valley* (Bristol, Adam Hilger, 1981).

Lloyd, Thomas, 'The architects of Regency Swansea', *Gower Journal*, 41 (1990).

Long, George E., 'Conversations with Richard Sullivan', *South Wales Evening Post*, 19, 21, 22 November 1956.

Matheson, Colin, 'William Robert Grove: Glamorgan physicist and judge', *Glamorgan Historian*, 9 (1973), 96–103.

Morgan, Hopkin, 'The trade of Llanelly', *Carmarthenshire Local History*, 2 (1962), 32–54.

Morgan, Prys, 'The Port Talbot district and the Blue Books of 1847', *Trans. Port Talbot and District Historical Society*, 3, 3 (1984), 84–97.

Morris, Bernard, 'More evidence for the date of Morris Castle', *South West Wales Indust. Archaeology Soc. Bull.*, 62 (1994), 4–5.

Morris, Bernard, *The Houses of Singleton* (Swansea, West Glamorgan Archives, 1995).

Newell, Edmund, 'Atmospheric pollution and the British copper industry, 1690–1920', *Technology and Culture*, 38 (1997), 655–89.

Newell, Edmund, 'Copperopolis: the rise and fall of the copper industry in the Swansea district, 1826–1921', *Business History*, 32 (1990), 75–97.

Newell, Edmund and Watts, Simon, 'The environmental impact of industrialisation in south Wales in the nineteenth century: 'Copper Smoke' and the Llanelli Copper Company', *Environment and History*, 2 (1996).

Parr, Gordon, *Man, Metals and Modern Magic* (Ames, Iowa State University Press, 1958).

Peters, E. D., *The Principles of Copper Smelting* (New York, 1907).

Percy, John, *Metallurgy* (London, John Murray, 1861).

Phillips, Rhys D., *The History of the Vale of Neath* (Neath, 1925).

'Pyrites', *The Copper Trade in Swansea*, 1860–1914 (Edinburgh, Waddie & Co., n.d.).

Rees, Gareth, 'Copper sheathing: an example of technological diffusion in the English merchant fleet', *Journal of Transport History*, 1 (1971–2), 85–94.

Rees, R., 'The Great Copper Trials', *History Today*, 43 (1993), 39–44.

Rees, R. 'The South Wales Copper-smoke Dispute, 1833–1895', *Welsh History Review*, 10, 4 (1981), 480–96.

Rees, William, *Industry before the Industrial Revolution* (Cardiff, University of Wales Press, 1968).

Reynolds, Paul, 'Blaen Pelenna Peat Charcoal Works', *South West Wales Indust. Archaeology Soc. Bull.*, 35 (1984), 4–6.

Reynolds, Paul, 'Industrial health in nineteenth century Swansea', *South West Wales Indust. Archaeology Soc. Bull.*, 43 (1986), 3–5.

Ridd, Tom, 'Swansea's barrow boys and girls', *Gower Journal*, 17 (1967), 51–3.

Ridd, Tom 'Gabriel Powell: the uncrowned king of Swansea', *Glamorgan Historian*, 5 (1969), 153–60.

Rogers, James, *A Sketch of the Cholera Epidemic at Ystalyfera in the Autumn of 1866* (Swansea, 1867).

Ross, J. R., *Letters from Swansea* (Llandybïe, Christopher Davies, 1969).

Roberts, R. O., 'The development and decline of copper and other non-ferrous metal industries in south Wales', *Trans. Hon. Soc. Cymmrodorion* (1955), 78–115.

——, 'Penclawdd Brass and Copper Works: a link with the slave trade', *Gower Journal* 14 (1961), 35–41.

——, 'The White Rock Copper and Brass Works, near Swansea, 1736–1806', *Glamorgan Historian*, 12 (n.d), 136–51.

Rowlands, John, *Copper Mountain* (Llangefni, Anglesey Antiquarian Society, 1966).

Smith, G. C. E. and Gibson, M. E., 'Yellow fever in south Wales, 1865', *Medical History*, 30 (1986) 322–40.

Stewart, Averil, *Family Tapestry* (London, J. Murray, 1961).

Hoskin, David and Sabine, Jennifer, *Swansea Cape Horners Remember* (Swansea, Maritime and Industrial Museum, n.d.).

Symons, M. V., *Coalmining in the Llanelli Area* (Llanelli, 1978).

Toomey, R. R., *Vivian and Sons, 1809–1924* (New York and London, Garland, 1985).

Thomas, Norman L., *Swansea's Districts and Villages* (2 vols., Swansea, 1969).

Thomas, Peter H., 'Medical men of Glamorgan: Thomas Williams of Swansea, 1818–1865', *Glamorgan Historian*, 10 (1973), 70–95.

Tomos, Dafydd, *Michael Faraday in Wales* (Denbigh, Gwasg Gee, 1973).

Trott, C. D. J., 'Coalmining in the borough of Neath', *Morgannwg*, 13 (1989), 47–74.

Turnbull, David, *Cuba* (London, Longmans, 1840).

Vivian, J. H., 'An account of the process of smelting copper as conducted at the Hafod Works', *Annals of Philosophy*, 5 (1823), 113–24.

Walker, Margaret, 'The British Association in Swansea in 1848', *Gower Journal*, 22 (1971), 14–24.

Warner, Rev. Richard, *A Second Walk through Wales* (London, 1799).

Webber, Vivian, *Journal of a Voyage round Cape Horn* (Swansea, 1859).

Williams, Glanmor (ed.), *Swansea: An Illustrated History* (Swansea, Christopher Davies, 1990).

Williams, Moelwyn I., 'Economic and social history of Glamorgan, 1660–1760', *Glamorgan County History*, 4 (Cardiff, 1980), 311–74.

Williams, Lionel, 'A sixteenth-century example of regional interdependence and alien participation in the mining industry: the exploitation of Cornish copper and lead ores and copper smelting at Neath, 1583–1587', *Morgannwg*, 3 (1959), 3–20.

Williams, Thomas, *A Sketch of the Relations which Subsist between the Three Kingdoms of Nature: the Mineral, Vegetable, and Animal* (Swansea, 1844).

Williams, Thomas, *Report on the Copper Smoke and its Influence on the Public Health and Industrial Diseases of Coppermen* (Swansea, 1854).

Wohl, Anthony S., *Endangered Lives in Victorian Britain* (Cambridge, Harvard University Press, 1983).

Wyndham, H. P., *A Gentleman's Tour through . . . Wales in the months of June and July 1774* (London, 1775).

Index